The End of the Future

The waning of the high-tech world

Jean Gimpel

Translated from the French by Helen McPhail

Adamantine Press Limited

Published in the United Kingdom in 1995 by *303.483 GIM*

Adamantine Press Limited
3 Henrietta Street
Covent Garden
London WC2E 8LU
England

Cover design Melby Document Presentation, Exeter, England
Page design Jim Turner Design and Management, Basingstoke, England
Project management and editing JG Editorial, Lincoln, England

British Library Cataloguing in Publication Data

A full catalogue record for this book is available from the British Library.

ISBN   0–7449–0117–0 cased
       0–7449–0118–9 paper

Composed in Linotron Palatino by Saxon Graphics, Derby, England

THE END OF THE FUTURE

The waning of the high-tech world

Contents

Introduction

The nineteenth-century maxim that 'You can't stop progress' is no longer accurate. It was once thought that progress was continuous and that history was moving faster, but this was no more than an illusion. Progress may not have come to a full stop but, today at least, it is moving at a noticeably reduced pace and its chances of speeding up again in the context of our civilisation are consequently non-existent.

Blind belief in continuous and accelerating progress reached its peak in the 1950s and 1960s. The list of predictions which have never been realised is long. We were told that by the year 2000 disease would be unknown; we would live to at least the age of 150; we would work four days a week or less and our chief concern would be how to fill our leisure time; we would spend our weekends on the Moon and interplanetary travel would be within the grasp of all.

Civilisations, however, move in cycles and the futurologists, like the economists, were wrong; both ignored the laws of technological and scientific development. Technology develops before science; but science continues to make advances when technology has ceased to evolve. At the end of a cycle in civilisation science loses ground while technology survives. In most cases the existence of these laws is unknown insofar as the history of technology is still in its infancy. (There is still no university chair of the history of technology anywhere in the world.)

The origin of the deep crisis affecting the West today lies in the very marked slow-down in technological innovation. An innovation is an invention which has been financed, tested, presented commercially and accepted by the market. The basic difference between an invention and an innovation is a phenomenon rarely discerned by economists and politicians or by scientists and engineers. This is why so few people understand that the West, like earlier forms of society, has reached a technological plateau.

This book aims to promote awareness of this phenomenon through the setback to futurologists' predictions, and also to explain what it is that allows the West to sustain itself for the time being on this technological plateau until the inevitable decline – through the revival of traditional technology modernised and revitalised by the most advanced technologies.

Rockets and propellers are enjoying a revival, as are airships and balloons, trains (the French TGV) and trams, ceramics and brick, cast iron and steel structures, chalk and blackboard, cotton and wool. It is of the greatest importance that industrial and economic leaders should be fully aware of this approach, in order to encourage research and investment in this lucrative and relatively under-exploited domain.

Our civilisation evolved like all its predecessors, each one believing that it could escape the fate of all others. History moves in cycles – this is the third theme of my book. Few historians have studied the mechanisms governing the evolution of these cycles, and fewer still have looked at the evolution of technologies and branches of science in past societies.

Modern society's enthusiasm for *Yesterday's Technology for Tomorrow*[1] marks a decisive turning-point for the West, the end of the industrial civilisation which began in the UK in the eighteenth century. Are we not also witnessing the approaching end of the scientific revolution which began in the seventeenth century; are we part of the swan-song of 'European exceptionalism'?[2]

---

1 Techniques d'hier pour demain, title of an exhibition suggested by Joël de Rosnay for the Cité des sciences et de l'industrie, March 1989.

2 The seminar 'European Exceptionalism', Harvard University, April 1989 organised by David Landes, author of *The Prometheus Unbound – Technical change and Industrial Development in Western Europe from 1750 to the Present*, (Cambridge, 1969).

THE END OF THE FUTURE

The waning of the high-tech world

CHAPTER 1

The Futures that Failed

In the thirteenth century, Roger Bacon drew up a plan for a vast reform of Christianity based on the prime importance of experimental science, mathematics and languages. He offered a vision of the future with automobiles, flying machines and submarines.

> Machines of navigation can be constructed, without rowers, as great ships for river or ocean, which are borne under the guidance of one man at a greater speed than if they were full of men. Also a chariot can be constructed that will move with incalculable speed without any draught animal ... Also flying machines may be constructed so that a man may sit in the midst of the machine turning a certain instrument, by means of which wings artificially constructed would beat the air after the manner of a bird flying. Also a machine of small size may be made for raising and lowering weights of almost infinite amounts – a machine of the utmost utility ... Machines may also be made for going in sea or river down to the bed without bodily danger ... and there are countless other things that can be constructed, such as bridges over rivers without pillars or any such supports ...[1]

The men of the Middle Ages were so mechanically minded that they believed in angels being answerable for the mechanisms of the universe: a Provençal manuscript depicts two winged angels operating the machinery which rotated the heavens.

The spirit of inventiveness that accompanied this outlook was only possible because medieval society believed in genuine progress, a concept unknown to the classical world. Medieval man in general refused to be tied down by tradition. As Gilbert de Tournai wrote:

> Never will we find truth if we content ourselves with what is already known... Those things that have been written before us are not laws but guides. The truth is open to all, for it is not yet totally possessed.[2]

---

[1] Quoted in S. Lilley, *Man, Machines and Men*, (Cobbett Press, 1948), p. 49.

[2] Jean Gimpel, *The Medieval Machine - the Industrial Revolution of the Middle Ages*, (London, 1992), p. 147.

And Bernard of Chartres of the episcopal school at Chartres 1114–19 said:

> We are dwarfs mounted on the shoulders of giants, so that although we perceive many more things than they, it is not because our vision is more precise or our stature higher, but because we are carried and elevated higher thanks to their gigantic size.[3]

The attitude exemplified by Gilbert de Tournai and Bernard of Chartres led their contemporaries to accept innovation as something normal and to assume that new inventions would always be forthcoming. The surgeon Theodoric wrote a treatise in 1267 in which, concerning the extraction of arrows, he comments: 'Every day a new instrument and a new method is invented.'[4]

In a sermon in 1306 in the church of Santa Maria Novella in Florence the Dominican Fra Giordano of Pisa sang the praises of the recent invention of eye-glasses. Fra Giordano said:

> Not all the arts have been found, we shall never see an end to finding them. Every day one could discover a new art ... It is not twenty years since there was discovered the art of making spectacles which help one to see well, an art which is one of the best and most necessary in the world. And that is such a short time ago that a new art which never before existed was invented ... I myself saw the man who discovered and practised it and I talked with him.[5]

Fra Giordano and Roger Bacon were – like we modern citizens of the late twentieth century – unknowingly entering an era of decline, of successive financial crises, with a marked drop in the number of innovations.

For a society to make economic progress requires more than invention and the patenting of inventions; these inventions must be realised in material terms and the public must want innovation. Yet since the days of the 'alternative' culture and, in France, since May 1968, the psychology of the French – as of the British and Americans – has changed, bringing a break with the materialistic future. This has passed unnoticed by economists – who are no longer front-page news and who have not learned the connection between the economy and mass psychology, the history of technology and science, or about cycles of civilisation.

Diminishing returns of technology

This extraordinary belief in progress, engendered in the medieval indus-

---

[3] Op. cit., pp. 147–8.

[4] Quoted in Lynn White, Jr., 'The Expansion of Technology 500–1000' in *The Fontana Economic History of Europe*, (London, 1969), vol. I, p. 24.

[5] Quoted in Lynn White, Jr., *Cultural Climates and Technological Advance in the Middle Ages*, (Viator, 1971), vol. II, p. 174.

trial revolution, which grew and expanded in the nineteenth and twentieth centuries, gave birth to the famous phrase, 'You can't stop progress'.
So much so that economists and futurologists were convinced that economic growth would continue steadily and that technological progress
would be linear. Their predictions have been proved wrong; we are witnessing today a marked slowing down of the world economy as well as
diminishing technological returns. A book which could have enlightened
them was published in 1978; this was *The Diminishing Returns of
Technology* by Orio Giarini and Henri Loubergié.[6]

Unfortunately the theme of the book went against the general trend of
the day and did not achieve the impact it should. Giarini and Loubergié
wrote:

> An exceptional period in human history came to an end around 1970.
> Although the economic growth of the past drew its strength from
> technical advances, the fact that technology now offers diminishing
> returns signifies not only that growth ossifies during the final period
> of innovation but also that it may be permanently disrupted.[7]

The authors quote some predictions made in the 1950s and 1960s which
have never been realised. In 1964 the Rand Corporation foretold that:

> 1971 was to be the year for achieving desalination of sea-water, 1972
> for automatic translation, 1974 for automatic air control, 1975 for the
> generalised use of teaching machines, 1975 for aircraft propulsion by
> nuclear reaction.[8]

These predictions, which will not be realised in our present civilisation,
may well be achieved in another civilisation just as Roger Bacon's predictions have materialised in this industrial cycle.

We are currently on a technological plateau, as in the Middle Ages at
the end of the thirteenth century and the first decades of the fourteenth
century. Development and innovation diminished considerably in that
period, except in the military domain, e.g. with the cannon.

This technological plateau which began at the end of the Middle Ages
was to last many centuries. It encompassed the Renaissance which was
not – contrary to general belief – conspicuous for its technological
progress, a fact which largely explains Leonardo da Vinci's failure to
have any of his 'inventions' transformed into actual innovations.
Following the research on Leonardo da Vinci as engineer by two historians of science and technology, Pierre Duhem (1861-1916) and Bertrand

---

[6] Orio Giarini and Henri Loubergié, *The Diminishing Returns of Technology*, (Oxford, 1978).

[7] Ibid., p. 17.

[8] Ibid., p. 64

Gille (1920-1980) and more recently by Paolo Galluzzi, director of the Instituto e Museo di Storia della Scienza, of Florence,[9] it is now increasingly accepted that in engineering terms he was no wizard. It was this fact which enabled the King of France to invite him to live at his Court; he was not wanted in Italy because he rarely finished what he had begun. Duhem, Gille and Galluzzi appear to indicate that Leonardo was a bookworm, and we would support this view. In fact Leonardo must have read Bacon's prophecies on flying machines in one of the many libraries where he worked; Bacon is specifically mentioned in one of his notebooks, now preserved in the British Museum. Bacon may thus have prompted him to draw such a machine.

Leonardo could have consulted a number of sketchbooks of engineering devices ranging from the early fourteenth century to the opening years of the sixteenth century, either in manuscript form or as printed books. These papers could perhaps be considered as the first venture into futurology. Most of the drawings of machines fall into three main categories: those that are improvements on contemporary High-Tech; those that would be realised in the nineteenth and twentieth centuries and those that will remain 'futures' without a future.

It should be specified that some of the advanced techniques adopted were of a military nature. As each cycle of a civilisation proceeds it can be seen that progress in civilian matters gives way to progress in armaments, as witnessed in our culture during recent decades. At such times gadgets proliferate, as happened in the Hellenistic era and during the Renaissance. Leonardo da Vinci was a master of the art of gadgetry for grand receptions and festivities.

There was nevertheless one military technique which was never adopted, a battle chariot driven by wind power. This was invented by Guy de Vigevano for the king of France, Philip VI of Valois who, in 1328, planned to go on a crusade. Vigevano's project excited the imagination of other Renaissance engineers, Taccola and Valturio, who also designed winged chariots: an example of a future that failed.

Vigevano also designed a boat in which oars were replaced by propellers, and bridges where pillars and other props were replaced by floating drums. Many of Vigevano's techniques were designed for prefabrication. Taccola, born in 1381, was the first engineer to illustrate a pair of hydraulic bellows and a suction and pressure pump.

The Manuscript of the Hussite War, written in about 1430, contains the first drawing of a cannon mounted on a carriage with two wheels, and the first known representation of a cannon on board a warship. The most remarkable of all the drawings is a handmill with a rod and crank

---

[9] In 1991, Galluzzi organised an exhibition in Sienna, *Primo di Leonardo* (Before Leonardo) - and in Avignon in 1992.

system; perhaps equally noteworthy is the drawing of a diver and his diving suit. This was not the first such illustration – akin to science fiction in that age – for Konrad Kyeser, born in 1366, had drawn two divers fighting under water:

> We have here a true piece of apparatus which is striking in its modernity. We can make out the waterproof tunic and lead-soled shoes, and the helmet shown in much less detail.[10]

One of the most remarkable Renaissance designs was an 'automobile' created by Francesco di Giorgio Martini. He also designed a hydraulic turbine which preceded the nineteenth-century Fourneyron turbine by some 350 years. Here we have the instance of a technique conceived in the fifteenth century but incapable of being constructed then because the engineers of the day lacked the technical and scientific skills required. Similarly, certain projects of our own time will only be realised in a future cycle of civilisation, when science and technology will have made giant strides. That will be an era for flirtation on Mars, for life on Earth at peace with mankind, and death without infirmity ...

Francis Bacon as futurologist

The prestige of scientific knowledge was enhanced by Sir Francis Bacon, who is famous for having written 'Knowledge is Power'. He was to write an imaginative essay, *The New Atlantis*, which was published in 1630, four years after his death. This was an Utopia or, as we would say today, a futurological essay, in which he described experiments which would not be realised before the nineteenth century or later. They included the prolongation of life, the successful treatment of incurable disease, the relief of pain. He foresaw too the possibility of:

> ... divers means of producing light ... of seeing objects afar off, as in the heavens ... help for the sight far above spectacles and glasses in use ... sound houses, where are practised and demonstrated all sounds and their generation ... means to convey sounds in trunks and pipes in strong line and distances ...flying in the air ...ships and boats for going under water ...[11]

Although Bacon was undoubtedly a man of the new modern age he was still immersed in the tradition of the Middle Ages, as can be seen in these references to flight and cruising under water. He was imbued with belief in progress and the fact that nature needed to be under control, a profoundly medieval attitude. It was the great US historian of medieval

---

[10] Bertrand Gille, *The Engineers of the Renaissance*, (Lund Humphries, 1966), p. 125.

[11] Quoted from Israel Levine, *Francis Bacon*, (Leonard Parsons, 1925), p. 178.

technology, Lynn White, who made the point that the way antiquity viewed nature contrasted with the Christian view of nature.

> In Antiquity ... every stream, every tree, every mountain contained a guardian spirit which had to be carefully propitiated before one put a mill in the stream or cut the trees or mined the mountain ...[12]

This medieval attitude to nature is one of the main underlying causes responsible for what Davis Landes, the author of *Prometheus Unbound*, has called European Exceptionalism – the western particularism which has helped to mark out the West as different from other civilisations.

Bacon's aphorism that 'knowledge is power' means that the final goal of science, to relieve all things possible, has led too many scientists in our contemporary world to justify their research without taking into account the dangers of their work for the future of mankind. What they do not know, or do not want to know, is that Francis Bacon had already, in his own day, been concerned about the dangers of certain experiments. He advocated that scientists should be bound by an oath.

> ... we have consultations, which of the inventions and experiences which we have discovered shall be published, and which not; and take all an oath of secrecy, for the concealing of those which we think fit to keep secret; though of those some we do reveal to the state and some not.[13]

What is tragic is that this proposal has gone unheeded. Whilst graduating medical doctors take their Hippocratic oath, scientists make no such promise. In the mid-1970s Professor M.W. Thring wrote a 'Hippocratic Oath for scientists' which is now promoted by Nicholas Albery, founder of The Institute for Social Inventions. We have followed this up by persuading Dr Federigo Mayor, the Director of UNESCO, to acknowledge the importance of such an Oath. He proposes that UNESCO should approach the relevant international organisations.[14]

If this heedlessness among scientists to such an oath is one of Bacon's failed futures, the fact that the influence of inventions on human life has not been pursued is another. So important did it seem to him that he resolved to devote part of his life opening men's eyes to it. He wrote:

> It is well to observe the force and effect and consequences of discoveries. These are to be seen nowhere more conspicuously than in those three which were unknown to the Ancients, and of which the origin,

---

[12] Lynn White, *Medieval Religion and Technology*, (California, 1975), p. 146.

[13] Benjamin Farrington, *Francis Bacon - Philosopher of Industrial Science*, (Lawrence and Wishart, 1951), p. 190.

[14] For information on the Oath, write to The Institute for Social Inventions, 24 Abercorn Place, London NW8 9XP.

though recent, is obscure; namely, printing, gunpowder and the magnet. For these three have changed the whole face and state of things throughout the world; the first in literature, the second in warfare, the third in navigation; whence have followed innumerable changes; insomuch that no empire, no sect, no star seems to have exerted greater power and influence in human affairs than these mechanical inventions.[15]

We should add that the very waning of discoveries in these final years of the twentieth century, which is one of the main themes of this book, is equally influential in human affairs and destiny.

Kepler, the first science fiction writer

The year of the first publication of *The New Atlantis*, 1630, was also the year of the death of Johannes Kepler, the great astronomer, mathematician and author of *Somnium* – The Dream. As Arthur Koestler wrote:

It is the first work of science fiction in the modern sense – as opposed to the conventional type of fantasy – utopias from Lucian to Campanella. Its influence on later authors of interplanetary journeys was considerable – from John Wilkins' *Discovery of a New World* and Henry More right down to Samuel Butler, Jules Verne and H.G. Wells.[16]

What is particularly remarkable about this book is Kepler's description of the physical and mental ordeals awaiting the space traveller:

The initial shock (of acceleration) is the worst part of it, for he is thrown upwards as if by an explosion of gunpowder ... Therefore he must be dazed by opiates beforehand; his limbs must be carefully protected so that they are not torn from him and the recoil is spread over all parts of his body. Then he will meet new difficulties: immense cold and inhibited respiration.[17]

It was not until May 1991 that a US space shuttle was launched into space with the aim of studying the effects of space on the human body.

Among those responsible for space programmes there has always been a tendency to underestimate the physiological effects of interplanetary travel. Astronauts were advised not to discuss their problems. The public was not properly aware of the scale of these problems posed by space until the Japanese journalist Akimaya was launched on a circuit of the Earth in a Soviet rocket. The list of ailments that afflicted him is a long

---

[15] Farrington, op. cit., p. 6.

[16] Arthur Koestler, *The Sleepwalkers*, (Harmondsworth, 1959), p. 421.

[17] Koestler, op. cit., p. 422.

one; and when his wife enquired one evening if he was all right, he answered 'Absolutely not OK'.

What Kepler did not foresee was the cost of a voyage to the moon. Living in the seventeenth century when economic problems were not the leading questions of the day, this is natural and excusable. Today's reduced number of space projects is linked to their cost, in part, but also to their increased complexity. In later chapters we shall see that many 'failed futures' are directly connected to the fact that these two problems have too often been severely under-estimated.

The failed futures of the 1950s and 1960s

In February 1955 the American General Nathan F. Twining announced an atomic plane capable of reaching any point on earth without refuelling, a pronouncement confirmed by the president of the US atomic energy commission. The aviation engine builders Pratt & Whitney had been commissioned to build a laboratory at Hartford, East Connecticut, while in England it was reported that the Harwell atomic energy laboratories had released technical information to two major aviation companies studying the possibility of nuclear-powered flight. The prospects seemed bright. John H. Hopkins, chairman of the US General Dynamics Corporation, confidently asserted that his generation would live to see atomic-powered airlines crossing the Atlantic in thirty minutes. Pessimists suggested fifteen years for this to be achieved, optimists reckoned on five. Informed observers tended to accept the latter estimate on the premise that 'up to now' in matters atomic, the optimists had usually been right.

In fact 1955 was a good year for travel prophesies. In January of that year Bell Aviation of Buffalo, NY, revealed plans for a commercial passenger rocket to make the transcontinental New York – San Francisco trip in 75 minutes. New York's *Cowles* magazine reported that the craft, with a maximum speed of 7,500 mph (12,000 kph) would be powered by eight engines. This dramatic passenger rocket craft was scheduled to make its maiden flight in 1961.

A few years earlier, in 1950, a Californian engineer, Theodore P. Hall, achieved a long-held ambition of many enthusiasts of the time when he succeeded in getting his family car airborne by means of wings, tail fin and light aero engine mounted on the roof. This most attractive technology unfortunately never took off commercially. The year 1958 witnessed another attempt at a flying jeep. It seemed the right moment to launch a flying vehicle, just as Henry Ford had in his day launched the Model T Ford. During the 1970s the technology of the ULM – the Ultra-Light Motor – was to revive this concept. But success was not just around the corner. As with so many projects for the future, technical success was thwarted by economic and social obstacles.

The 1960s saw the outline of an apparently realistic and beneficial solution to the problem of transport: the road that does the driving. However, this futuristic project barely got beyond the drawing board and initial prototype. It was reported from Princeton, New Jersey, that RCA engineers were experimenting with an electronic road which would steer cars moving along it and control their speed. This was a first step towards fully automated roads on which the driver would be able, if he wished, to sleep at the wheel without fear of accident.

Probably the strangest, although in the circumstances forgivable, failed predictions on road transport was the 1890s forecast that in thirty years' time the streets of New York would be two feet deep in horse droppings – because of the increase in traffic!

Hermann Kahn and Alvin Toffler's failed speculations

Two best-sellers concentrating on the future were published in the late 1960s and early 1970s: Hermann Kahn and Anthony Wiener's *The Year 2000 – a Framework for speculation on the next 33 years* and Alvin Toffler's *Future Shock*. It is instructive today to read or re-read the innovations predicted which never materialised and which will surely never see the light of day in our civilisation. Kahn and Wiener predicted:

> The use of nuclear explosives for excavations and mining – permanent lunar excavations – artificial moons and other methods for lighting large areas at night – human hibernation for relatively extensive periods (months to years) – commercial extraction of oil from shale – effective desalination on a large scale – life expectancy extended to 150 years – immortality?[18]

What is particularly extraordinary is that the authors not only believed, in 1967, in a linear technological progress but that they were convinced that it was increasing exponentially. More was to come, however, with the publication three years later of Alvin Toffler's *Future Shock*, in which he wrote:

> ... the roaring current of change, a current so powerful today that it overturns institutions, shifts our value and shrivels our roots[19] ... western society for the past 300 years has been caught up in a fire of change. This storm, far from abating, now appears to be gathering force. Change sweeps through the highly industrialised countries with waves of ever-accelerating speed and unprecedented impact.[20]

---

[18] Hermann Kahn and Anthony J. Wiener, *The Year 2000*, (London, 1968), pp. 51–5.

[19] Alvin Toffler, *Future Shock*, (London, 1970), p. 1.

[20] Ibid., p. 9.

The future visualised by Toffler never came about because it ran out of steam.

The diminishing returns of technology acknowledged

As mentioned at the opening of this chapter, the first authors to have realised the dramatic ebbing of technology were Giarini and Loubergié, who were writing in the last years of the 1970s. With the 1980s an increasing number of publications were to highlight this phenomenon. The Organisation of Economic Cooperation and Development (OECD), based in Paris and comprising most of the world's industrial nations, published in 1980 a report entitled *Changement technique et politique économique* (Technical Change and Economic Policy) in which we read:

> Technical progress cannot be taken for granted. Neither its pace nor its direction can currently be considered satisfactory. Its pace has slowed markedly.[21]

The authors of the report stress that one of the reasons for this state of affairs is the anti-technological and even anti-scientific ideology of the counter-culture, with its string of regulations relating to security and protection of the environment. These decisions have had dramatic consequences for the cost and pace of innovation, notably affecting the pharmaceutical and pesticides industries.

> Despite the considerable growth in research and development in the pharmaceutical industry over the last fifteen years, the number of new chemicals introduced on to the United States market dropped by about half between 1960 and 1973. The cost of undertaking the development and trial of a pharmaceutical innovation (a new chemical product) has risen in current prices from some $1.2m to $24m between 1962 and 1974, and to $54m in 1976, according to latest estimates.[22]

In the following year Jean-Jacques Salomon, who participated in the OECD report, published *Promethée empêtré* (Prometheus Entangled), a very interesting book subtitled *La Résistance au changement technique* (Resistance to Technological Change). In this he points out that now Prometheus – the demigod who made man from clay, stole fire from Olympus and taught man how to use it:

---

[21] *Changement technique et politique économique*, Organisation de coopération et de développement économiques, 2, rue André-Pascal, 75016 Paris, p. 17.

[22] Ibid., p. 54.

... should reckon not only with the resistance of things, of matter, of nature, but also with the resistance of man, of institutions and of cultures. Entangled, embarrassed and even dragged along by the successes encouraging his aptitude for creation and innovation, man is halted at a barrier marked out by those very people whose living conditions he is doing his utmost to transform.[23]

As indicated above, our industrial civilisation has been heavily influenced by the 1960s. The ecology movement which appeared during that decade and which now affects a high percentage of western society, deflected both the young and the less young from cities and industry towards nature, while the cult of gadgets and innovation ceased to fascinate the masses. In consequence the industrialist who launches new products more sees them rejected by his customers. Inevitably his turnover is reduced and he is forced to lay off some of his work-force. The current world crisis is largely the result of the evolution in western attitudes. We predicted this evolution in 1956, during a lecture at Yale on the parallels between the Middle Ages and the USA; it will be discussed more extensively in chapter 8, *The Relentless Cycles of History*. We foretold then that what we have referred to as 'society's psychological drive' would increasingly tend to restrict development in that country, before affecting Europe a few years later. The movement is irreversible.

The economy polluted by ecologists

By the early 1970s the American economist Sidney Rolfe was aware of the harmful ways in which ecologists might affect the economy. He wrote that 'Excessive environmentalism pollutes the economy' – but the word 'excessive' is itself unnecessary.

Sidney Rolfe was to offer the first example of an ecological project which, if put into practice, would have entailed the redundancy of many workers. In the early 1970s US ecologists decided to clean up the river Mahoning near Youngstown, Ohio, by putting pressure on the owners of late nineteenth-century steel works. The aim was to force them to treat waste materials so that the river could once more support trout, as it had done in 1850. But the cost of treatment equipment would have forced the factories to dismiss thousands of workers, and probably to close down. An opponent of the ecologists looked in the archives and discovered that there had never been trout in the river Mahoning in 1850 ...

Many of the figures advanced by environmentalists are similarly based on false assertions. Nothing is currently less certain than the theory of

23 Jean-Jacques Salomon, *Prométhée Empêtré - La Résistance au changement Technique*, (Paris, 1982), p. 4.

global warming. Europe in the twelfth and thirteenth centuries was a degree or two warmer than today; this was the period when vines could be grown in Yorkshire, in the north of England.

Pollution and the destruction of the environment are not new problems. They were known in medieval times.

> The glass industry demolished the woods for fuel for its furnaces, and the iron industry needed charcoal for its forges[24]... The extent of the damage caused by iron smelters to forests can be appreciated when one realises that to obtain approximately 50 kilograms of iron it was necessary at that time to reduce approximately 200 kilograms of iron ore with as much as 25 cubic metres of wood. It has been estimated that in forty days, one furnace could level the forest for a radius of 1 kilometre.[25]

Urban rivers were polluted by slaughterhouses. The Seine in 1293 was polluted by the slaughter of 188,522 sheep, 30,116 oxen, 19,604 calves, and 30,784 pigs. The Seine and other European rivers were also polluted by tanning, an operation which consisted of subjecting hides to a whole series of chemical treatments requiring tannic acids or lime. Tawing used alum and oil. Dried blood, fat, surplus tissues, flesh impurities and hair were continually washed away with the acids and the lime into the streams running through the cities. The water flowing from the tanneries was certainly unpalatable and there were tanneries in every medieval city.

As today, measures were voted through to protect the environment and prevent pollution. By the end of the thirteenth century, to reduce deforestation, there was a ban on the use of the hydraulic powered saw, the first two-stroke machine, at Colmars in the 'Alpes-de-Haute-Provence'. A century later, in 1388, the English parliament in session in Cambridge passed the first national anti-pollution law relating to water and air. London, at the end of the thirteenth century, had the sad distinction of being the first city in the world to suffer from atmospheric pollution. The law specified that all waste materials were to be taken outside the city 'otherwise the air ... is greatly corrupt and infect and many Maladies and other intolerable Diseases do daily happen'.[26] Because the word 'pollution' did not yet exist, the English text describes the 'impayring and corrupcion of the said water of the rever biforesaid'.

Is it purely by chance that, in our declining era, we are taking measures to protect the environment, as was done at the end of the Middle

---

[24] Jean Gimpel, *The Medieval Machine*, op. cit., pp. 75–6.

[25] Ibid., p. 79.

[26] G.C. Coulton, *Social Life in Britain from the Conqueror to the Reformation*, (Cambridge, 1918), p. 330.

Ages? With greater age there is an increasing tendency to act conservatively, occasionally to an excessive extent. It is clear that certain decisions designed to protect the environment in North Africa have for some years led to the reappearance of one of the biblical plagues – swarms of locusts. The use of the insecticide Dieldrin succeeded in restricting their devastations; but the use of this product was forbidden, to be replaced by an insecticide considered less harmful to wildlife, Fenitrothion. The consequence is that millions of humans from the Atlantic to the Indian Ocean and from the Mediterranean to the southern Sahel spend every year in terror that the locusts will return, with all the ensuing dramatic economic consequences. The description of this plague in Exodus is now once more, tragically, of current concern. As the result of excessive caution and love, we have taken a three-thousand-year step backwards.

> ... tomorrow will I bring the locusts into thy coasts:
> And they shall cover the face of the earth, that one cannot be able to see the earth: and they shall eat the residue of that which escaped, which remaineth unto you from the hail, and shall eat every tree which groweth for you out of the field.[27]

In an article in *The New Scientist* we read that:

> The UN is losing its war against locusts. Agricultural scientists meeting in the Netherlands in December claimed that in the late 1980s one of the biggest locust plagues on record was stopped only because strong winds blew the locusts into the sea. The UN's $400m programme to combat the locusts, which relied heavily on satellite imaging, achieved little, they said.[28]

Liability laws versus innovation

Ecologists are obviously not alone in their responsibility for this slowing down of technological progress in the western world as we approach the end of the twentieth century. Legislation in the USA during the 1960s and 1970s, of the kind known in the UK as 'civil responsibility' and in the USA as 'liability' or 'tort law', is undermining innovation. The USA, which was a leader in twentieth-century technical progress, is no longer creative. Under the pressure of lawyers and judges the liability laws are alarmingly in the ascendant.

This has created what are known in the USA – and also now in the UK – as 'ambulance chasers', lawyers who hasten after ambulances to be the first professional on the scene of an accident. They press their offers of

---

[27] Exodus X, 4–5.

[28] 'Locusts win War with UN' *New Scientist*, 8 January 1994.

service on the accident victim, free of charge in return for 50 per cent of any damages won. The sum involved may not uncommonly reach $1m; it is therefore hardly surprising that US students are more interested in the law than in scientific studies.

The vertiginous increase in settlements during recent years encourages all and sundry to go to law. There is no risk, except for the 50 per cent portion of any damages paid to your lawyer if he is successful. If you fall off a ladder, even if you were at fault you may be able to sue the manufacturer for damages; hardly surprising, then, that the manufacturers have increased their prices by 30 per cent. This 'tax' – which is what it is in effect – is:

> ... responsible for one quarter of the price of a ride on a Long Island tour and one third of the price of a small airplane ... and over 95 per cent of the price of childhood vaccines.[29]

Peter Huber, who struggles in the USA against this plague of liability laws, writes that if they had existed in the past our society would have been incapable of making industrial progress.

> The Wright Brothers wouldn't get off the ground to-day ... and had Henry Ford tried to introduce the Model T in 1987, he probably wouldn't have made it. Darn thing is dangerous; why, you can break your arm cranking it up.[30]

It should be made clear that these laws are the result of the US legal system, in which cases are debated before a jury; this restricts innovation by discouraging all novelty. New technologies are handicapped because the old is innocent until proven guilty, while the new is *a priori* guilty unless and until proven innocent.

> Age, familiarity and ubiquity are the most potent legitimising forces known to the modern Liability system. The inexpert juror is predisposed to spot 'defects' in technologies that are unfamiliar and adventuresome.[31]

The consequence is that many new products are better and safer than the old, but they are condemned not to be made commercially available while older and less reliable techniques survive and prosper.

---

[29] Peter W. Huber, *Liability - The Legal Revolution and its Consequences*, (New York, 1988), p. 3.

[30] Peter W. Huber, 'Memo to scientists: stop innovating' *The Scientist*, 11 January 1988.

[31] Peter W Huber, 'Who will Protect us Against our Protectors', *Forbes*, 13 July 1987, p. 64.

CHAPTER 2

Mythinformation or the Computer Bluff

'Have the millions of computers purchased by US businesses brought any overall improvement in productivity? Surprisingly, the best information available says no ...'[1] The marked slowing down of investment in information technology and telecommunications since the mid-1980s in the USA may perhaps be explained by the lack of growth in white-collar productivity. This has increasingly entailed restructuring in the computer industry, with tens or even hundreds of thousands of workers being laid off. Paradoxically, a number of US companies are shelving a high percentage of their computers in order to increase their productivity.

The deep financial crisis in the computer world, with shares crashing on the Stock Exchange and businesses closing down or going bankrupt, is partly the result of too much futurology in the late 1970s and early 1980s. This was the period when countless books and magazines proclaimed loud and clear that we were embarking on a new Era of Mankind comparable to the Industrial Revolution: this was the Information Revolution.

The expression 'revolution' kept on reappearing. We were living through a revolution in micro-electronics, in information networks, in computers. The ecstasy reached a climax when, in 1982, Time magazine selected the computer as its 'Man of the Year' – but this was to be short-lived and 1983 marked the beginning of the end of this 'Glorious Revolution'.

Unlike the British industrial revolution, this was not a 'revolution' that would change 'where and how people worked, lived, thought, played and prayed':[2] it was to be a form of technical progress which would stay with us permanently. However, as was confirmed by a report published in 1986 by the Agence de l'informatique (ADI),[3] the computer is an élitist technology, of value only to those who can genuinely master it. For

---

[1] William Bowen, 'The Puny Pay-off from Office Computers', *Fortune*, 26 (1986).

[2] Melvin Kranzberg, 'The Information Age' in *Computers in the Human Context*, (Oxford, 1989), p. 20.

[3] As reported in *Le Monde*, 7 January 1986.

everyone else, on the other hand, it represents inflexibility and excessive cost.[4]

The myth of the electronic cottage

The revolution predicted by the futurologists consisted of the happy return of 'alienated' office workers to the home-based work of the pre-industrial revolution era, with the computer terminal replacing the spinning wheel. One of the most famous contemporary futurologists, Alvin Toffler, described the coming of the electronic cottage era with enthusiasm in another futuristic book, *The Third Wave*:

> Hidden inside our advance to a new production system is a potential for change so breathtaking in scope that few among us have been willing to face up to its meaning ... a return to cottage industry on a new, higher electronic basis and with it a new emphasis on the home as the center of society ... the fight for the electronic village is part of a larger super-struggle between the Second Wave past and the Third Wave future.[5]

There was never even the beginning of a fight. It too was a non-starter.

One of the earliest works to evaluate the problems posed by the social integration of computerism was published in France in 1984. The authors raised the alarm:

> The integration of a new technology into a way of life does not follow the simple laws of mechanics... the scenery is not transformed overnight simply because the technical revolution exists.[6] ... The timespan required for practical development, for distribution and above all for the 'socialisation' of these potential innovations – i.e. for their integration into our way of life through spreading practice and specific uses – renders their true impact an unlikely event for the next 20 years.[7]

Yet this failed great project was to bring about the first serious crisis in the computer industry, which had invested heavily in the home computer. Home computers had of course been sold, but it was rumoured a few years ago that 30 per cent of the machines ended up on the shelf, and it was said that the most lucrative part of the business was the sale of cupboards to put them in.

---

[4] I wrote this book on my word-processor, which I think I know how to use ...

[5] Alvin Toffler, *The Third Wave*, (London, 1981), pp. 204–5.

[6] P.A. Mercier, F. Plassard and V. Scardigli, *La Société digitale - les nouvelles technologies au futur quotidien*, (Paris, 1984), p. 7.

[7] Ibid., p. 12.

In the *Washington Post* dated 7 April 1985 Tim Miller headed an article: 'The Truth about Home Computers – Straight talk from the Experts on why so many Home Computers are a waste of time.' In this he wrote: 'A computer company director – Gary Kildall, chief executive of Digital Research – says that a lot of home computers are being used as doorstops these days.' This was confirmed by Steve Wozniak, co-founder of the Apple Computer Company: 'There's very little productivity in home computers ... there are a lot of times I spend twice as many hours only because I am doing it with a computer and not with prior methods which worked better.' Miller, the freelance journalist, concluded his work on the *Washington Post* article in unfriendly terms: malfunction in his word processor had destroyed transcriptions of six hours of interviews.

As I have indicated, the failure in home computers was not so much technical as social and psychological. One of the best books on the subject in the English-speaking world is Tom Forester's *Computers in the Human Context*.[8] In his foreword Forester quotes the figure of more than $300bn a year being spent on computers and associated software while only about 300 researchers were engaged in investigating the effects on the economy and on society at large (1989 figures).

It is the human factor which decides the difference between success and failure in the implementation of Information Technology (IT); and it is precisely this human factor which has brought about the downfall of home computers. Forester appears to have discovered this factor for himself after seven years of working at home:

> After an initial honeymoon period of 2–3 years which was accompanied by feelings of elation and productivity it was followed by feelings of loneliness, isolation and a growing desire to escape the same 'four walls'.[9]

In 1987 he gave up full time home-work in an attempt to solve this problem and took a part-time job on a computer journal. As observed by William Atkinson, who has studied relationships between the home-worker and the family, 'Home working was rarely viewed favourably by the wives of homeworking husbands'. 'You ought to interview wives too. They're the ones who have to deal with the problems,' was the comment of the wife of one of his interviewees.[10] The 'problem' consists of a serious psychological drain on families.

---

[8] Tom Forester, *Computers in the Human Context - Information Technology Productivity and People*, (Oxford, 1989).

[9] Ibid, p. 218

[10] William Atkinson, 'Working at Home - Is it for you', (Homewood, IL, 1985), in Forester, op. cit. pp. 218–9.

Home shopping via the home computer 'has not come up to expectations because it does not fulfil the psychological needs of shoppers. For home-based women or men, stuck indoors all day, going out to the shops or to the bank is a safety-valve despite all the drawbacks of modern shopping'.[11] As will be seen at the end of this chapter, France's Minitel system is an exception.

In the USA, banking services via home computers have largely failed, with many banks withdrawing from the system even though, when the service was introduced, it was proclaimed as the greatest discovery since the deposit slip. Chase Manhattan, the City Corporation and the Chemical Bank all invested considerable sums in the personal computer (PC) boom; banks dreamed of millions of wealthy clients happily paying a premium to avoid going to the bank in person or writing cheques. But, like many dreams, the PC banking service has faded.

By 1989 only thirty-six US banks were still offering this service, against seventy in the early 1980s: only a tiny fraction of households with a PC still subscribed to the system. Even some of the pioneering banks have withdrawn. PC banking is perceived to be an indulgence, a class medium rather than a mass medium.

Information technology and declining productivity

Banks and the financial sector in the USA, dreaming of substantial growth in productivity and profits gained from massive investment in computers, were the US economic leaders in adopting this new technology. The dream, however, remained a dream: while users struggled to operate the new systems, capital productivity and profitability diminished.

> Output growth in the financial industry in the US was 4.7 per cent from 1948 to 1958 but declined to 3.6 per cent coincident with the expansion of computers' use from 1958 to 1983. Capital input rose fourteen-fold, growing 2.7 per cent/year up to 1958 but 9.8 per cent/year thereafter with investment increasingly concentrated in computers ... Labor hours rose almost threefold overall. After 1958, with decreased output growth and increased capital investment, a decline in the growth rate of labor might have been expected. Instead the growth rate of labor rose slightly from 2.8 per cent/year before 1958 to 3.1 per cent/year over the next quarter century.[12]

---

[11] Forester, *Computers*, op. cit. p. 221.

[12] Richard H Franke, 'Technological Revolution and Productivity Decline: The case of US Banks' in Forester, *Computers*, op.cit. p. 283.

Although historically the banks were the most experienced users of information systems, they have encountered difficult times in their efforts to improve productivity from what now represents an additional annual investment of $30bn. Assessed by traditional methods, investment in information systems has not improved banking productivity.

Misuse of business computers can in fact significantly reduce productivity, as seen in the experience of a young French manager living and working in London. Alain Strasser, UK director of a US company with a workforce of 1,500, including 250 in Ireland, was anxious to know why productivity was declining in Ireland despite improvement in the English factories. He flew to Ireland to meet the Irish manager who, at every question, turned to his computer screen before answering. This curious dialogue continued for almost an hour, and Strasser soon realised that the reduction in productivity was the result of the manager's losing all human contact with his employees. The computer had taken over.

Back to chalk

Contrary to all expectations, the computer has not taken over in education, either in the USA or elsewhere, although the IT revolution was expected to have arrived by now.

In the early 1980s, enthusiasts predicted that children would soon be learning more from computers than they had ever learnt from teachers. But in the USA today, after expenditure of more than $3bn on an estimated 1.7m personal computers, educators are tending to halt the undertaking and to cancel the predicted revolution in schools.

The shortage of software suitable for teaching is a serious obstacle. Because the market is less remunerative than in business the choice of programs remains somewhat limited as well as being slower and less simple to operate. Persuading teachers to use computers in the classroom is another considerable difficulty. Few teachers criticise computers publicly for fear of appearing technologically backward – a phenomenon frequently encountered, the fear of appearing 'anti-technology'. In recent years the computer world has brainwashed people into believing that to be anti-computers is to be backward-looking and out of date. Anyone who criticises computers is almost sure to be ageing ...

In France, the most technologically-advanced nation in the world in the 1970s and 1980s, educationalists failed to introduce computers into classrooms as a general rule because the software is poor in quality and offers little benefit to pupils. The commission which evaluated educational progress in France, testing 260 educational programs over a period of two years, reported that 20–30 per cent were of very poor quality and 10 per cent excellent, although overall quality was tending to improve.

Big deal! The situation was scarcely better in other countries; only 12 per cent of the 10,000 teaching programs in use in the USA were genuinely satisfactory.

We may wonder how to judge such assessments, since the effectiveness of a program depends equally on pupils and teacher. At the present time teachers appear too easily satisfied with the programs currently available, and software companies therefore lack the impetus to improve their material. It is perhaps not surprising that the French company FIL, creators of educational software with a major shareholding in the hands of the testing commission mentioned above, went bankrupt in 1988.

As these new means of audiovisual expression fail to take off it is scarcely surprising to learn that they have equally failed to eliminate chalk in the classroom – quite the opposite, in fact, for its use is returning after a period of decline. Every year millions of teachers use more than 1,500 tonnes of chalk in their schools. The blackboard has returned to favour, ousting the felt-tipped pen and white screen. Anxious to save money, schools have realised with alarm than the white screens are much more costly to use; this growing trend in France is already clearly apparent in Germany where the sale of blackboards has grown by 8 per cent per year since the beginning of the 1990s.

Today's chalk shows improvements over yesterday's product; technical advances based on laboratory research have eliminated its squeakiness and introduced a specially impregnated cloth which absorbs the chalkdust. In the push-button factory of Omya Color, creators of these improvements, eight workers produce two million sticks of chalk every day.

And the blackboard is a far more effective instrument for putting across a lecturer's message than a projector, which frequently masks laziness and poor communication skills. The audience can follow the speaker's argument better if he writes up his reasoning on the blackboard.

Back to work

Computers were supposed to liberate man from the drudgery of work. We were to live in a leisure society with analysts and counsellors teaching people how to enjoy their newfound leisure time. It is disheartening to realise that these futurological predictions have not been fulfilled. We were to work fewer hours – but now we can perceive that this is not happening. In fact, according to the US Bureau of Labor statistics, exactly the opposite appears to have taken place over the past decade. Wage earners tend to work as hard, or harder, than before. A Harris poll has established that Americans' leisure time decreased by 8.5 hours per week

---

[13] Forester, *Computers*, op. cit. p. 7.

between 1978 and 1985.[13]

Robots were to take over the running of our society, but this too has not occurred. We must remember that many predictions come from people who are promoting their own products; many of those who predicted a world run by robots were themselves robot manufacturers. In 1968 they forecast a US population of 100,000 robots by 1972, but twenty years later the USA had only 20,000, with perhaps 100,000 world-wide. In 1975 a very reputable business agency, Frost and Sullivan, estimated that in 1980 the European robot industry would have a 2 billion franc turnover – but when 1980 came, the same agency published a new market report in which they accepted that the industry's turnover was no more than FF195m: an estimating error of 1:10 in five years.

A return to human intelligence

It is therefore hardly surprising that some US robot manufacturers went out of business, while one 'showcase' installation, the John Deere farm machinery factory in Iowa, turned out to be a complete disaster.

> The reason for this state of affairs is not hard to find: people get carried away with Utopian visions of automated factories, overlooking the high costs of High Tech and the enormous complexity of factory operations. Robots were absurdly over-hyped: it was conveniently ignored that they are both much more expensive and much less flexible than humans.[14]

When the USA realised in the mid-1970s that Japan was overtaking them industrially, emissaries were despatched to discover, on the spot, the reasons for this impressive takeoff. The Japanese explained to the US managers that the human factor was the major element in their success – but the Americans kept looking for technological solutions and did not come round to the Japanese point of view for several years. It is only recently that the USA has begun to consider human factors in industry, but in most cases it is already too late.

In the early 1980s the French too discovered the essential role of the human factor in the Japanese industrial expansion. They recognised that the fundamental reason for Japanese growth was the very high national level of education, indeed the highest in the world. The report of a French team, headed by Thierry Gaudin, published in 1983, on 'The Intelligence Revolution'[15], urged the French government to recognise the prime importance of education and training. The following year the

---

[14] Ibid., p. 10.

[15] *The Intelligence Revolution – a European Report on the State of Technology*, translated and adapted by the Gamma Institute Press, Canada.

French government resolved that, by the year 2000, 80 per cent of students should reach the baccalauréat level, equivalent to two years of college education in the USA or college entrance standard in the UK, a major step towards the intellectualisation of technology advocated by the report.

Japanese industry therefore owes its success neither to the computer nor to the robot, although they have of course contributed to its expansion. As Konosuke Matsushita, a senior manager with the Matsushita Electric Company, stated in 1979:

> Your organisations are Taylorist ... We are Post-Taylorist ... Our major corporations give their personnel three or even four times as much training as you do; it is for this reason that they encourage internal dialogue and communication, invite suggestions from one and all and demand that the educational system prepare an increasing number of university graduates, because enlightened and cultured generalists represent an indispensable resource for industries which must rely on permanent intelligence.[16]

Its high level of education has enabled Japan to upgrade certain traditional technologies, such as metal casting, through the application of advanced technology. As early as the 1970s employees in Japanese steelmills were using pocket calculators to check electric furnaces producing cast iron, thereby reducing a process requiring four hours in Europe to only one hour and forty minutes in Japan. Europe has now followed suit:

> Steel mills are computer-controlled at the Usinor plant in Dunkirk, continuous casting is monitored on a screen, the computer calculates both the material and heat flow and provides continuous information on the distribution of molten or solidified zones in the metal.[16]

The mirage of Artificial Intelligence

Paradoxically, in 1981 the Japanese – whose economy has been been dominated by the computer – launched an ambitious ten-year programme for a 'fifth generation' computer capable of processing knowledge rather than figures, performing more reliably and efficiently than human operators. Their aim was to create nothing less than Artificial Intelligence (AI). The world press came out with headlines proclaiming Utopia: 'Computers will empty offices,' 'Computers ready to make mankind redundant'. The Japanese were to discover that computers, however sophisticated, can never replace human intelligence and

---

[16] Ibid., p. 7.

instinctive expertise, or reproduce innate physical skills.

> After ten years and an investment of $400m, all Japan has produced is a handful of parallel computers, 10 layers of which have only a quarter of the target number of processors and only a number of computer experts know how to operate them... The US researchers found them to be slow, cryptic and filled with bugs.[17]

In the USA computers are now essentially doorstops that are used mostly for electronic mail.

Can the computer be tamed?

Artificial Intelligence will therefore not replace human intelligence in the foreseeable future – if ever; but the use of computers is gradually revealing the limits of our own intellect. The innumerable problems posed by the computer are so varied and complex that we are forced to wonder whether we have reached the limits of our relationship with technology. For thousands of years man has progressively mastered technology in order to create a better world – at least in the advanced nations – but as time goes by we are gradually realising that we cannot tame the computer.

The simplest form of program, word processing, can be difficult to manage. Disks are apparently full when they should still have space available, files carefully saved on disk disappear or suddenly become irretrievable. Power cuts, fluctuations in voltage or radio and television signals may upset the computer. In an article headed 'Me and My Word processor', the writer Tom Sharpe wrote:

> Leave a floppy disk next to a loud-speaker or something with a strong magnetic force and you can lose an entire novel. True, you can, if you are Carlyle, lend Mill the manuscript of your *French Revolution* and have a cleaning lady, with more discrimination than she knew, burn the damned thing, but I've always felt she must have lit a great many fires to get rid of the lot. So paper burns, says the WP merchant: where's the difference? In my inability to know a magnetic force when I'm near one.[18]

France had 31,000 recorded computer breakdowns during 1987 – an average of more than 80 per day, each representing a loss for the company involved of FF8–14m: these figures represent only part of the probable damage. 'Silence is golden in this domain' according to the chairman of the French computer security group which supplied the figures.[19] In

---

[17] 'Japan stubs its toes on fifth generation computers', *Nature*, 26 March 1992.

[18] Tom Sharpe, 'Me and my Word Processor', *The Listener*, 25 April 1985.

[19] 'Informatique: les perceurs de secrets', *L'Express*, 3 March 1988, 95.

cases of total computer loss 20 per cent of managing directors estimate the life expectancy of their company at a few hours and 48 per cent a few days. These alarming figures were revealed by an enquiry covering 500 companies, carried out in February 1988 by MSD, a division of Arthur Young International, for the European Union.

For anyone who wishes to see for himself the malfunction of all too many computers, a visit to the Cité des Sciences et de l'Industrie, one of France's leading scientific and cultural centres, will show that 'between 30 and 40 per cent of the automatic equipment (interactive audiovisual games) are always out of service and awaiting repair'.[20] Is there a link between these figures and the fact that in a letter to me on 13 March 1988 the development director of the Cité des Sciences, Joël de Rosnay, suggested an exhibition on the theme of 'Yesterday's technology for tomorrow'?

Thousands of incidents were left out of the figures published in 1987. Frequently, indeed, public services, industry and other private companies prefer to protect their reputation by not revealing that the smooth running of their administration has increasingly often been disrupted by their own employees.

Computer problems are not solely derived from their software but are increasingly created by their users; it has been estimated that up to 60 per cent of computer vandalism is perpetrated within the company.[21] The lure of profit is not the employee's only motivation: promotion refused; apparently unjustified redundancy; early enforced retirement; nervous depression – all may be causes. In many countries the workforce is well aware of the computer's prime importance in running the business. The staff of one substantial company became famous through organising a sit-in within the central computer room in order to force a general rise in salary from the management – who realised how much the company was losing each day through the non-availability of its computer system and swiftly agreed to pay. The employee poses a serious threat in terms of controlling computers, for no security measures can ever guarantee total protection.

In an article headed 'Burglars swap crowbars for computers', Gary Bloombecker, director of the National Center for Computer Crime Data in Los Angeles, was quoted as saying, 'the wise computer security professional should worry less about teenage hackers and more about ordinary criminals and employees'.[22] More 'professional' criminals now rely on computers for their criminal activity, particularly for embezzlement and industrial espionage. Some computer crimes may be amusing, others less

---

[20] Yves Lasfarge, *Technojolies, Technofolies*, (Les Editions d'organisation, 1988), p. 127.

[21] Philippe Rosé, *La Criminalité informatique*, (Paris, 1988).

[22] 'Burglars swap crowbars for computers', *New Scientist*, 8 April 1989.

so. A fraudster working in collusion with an agricultural chemicals sales-man managed to change the computer data in a weather forecasting centre, which duly announced, wrongly, a forecast of rain during the har-vest season. Farmers hurried to order tonnes of chemicals to prevent rot-ting, which proved to be entirely unnecessary and which cost the farmers FF3m. Less diverting is the way in which the Mafia penetrated IBM's con-fidential information centre, even though it was protected by fingerprint identification; one of the managers was kidnapped, his index finger cut off and his fingerprints used to penetrate the IBM network for two weeks.

A third form of damage which, unlike the other two, has made front page news, is the hacker who introduces a virus into the world's com-puter networks. Such computer viruses have been compared with AIDS. Any virus, whether biological or electronic, is basically a disorder of information systems. The biological virus is a tiny scrap of genetic code – DNA or RNA – capable of taking over the machinery of the living cell and turning it into thousands of perfect replicas of the original virus.

Like its biological counterpart, the computer virus carries in its instruc-tion code the recipe for making perfect copies of itself. Lodged in a host computer, the virus takes control of the system and when the infected computer is subsequently in contact with a healthy piece of software a fresh copy of the virus passes into the new program. Thus the infection spreads from one computer to another and the potential for widespread contagion is enormous.

To date the most famous virus episode occurred in November 1988, jamming one of the US' most powerful networks, ARPANET, and paralysing over six thousand computers for two days right across the country. Dozens of military and civilian installations were hit, including the Lawrence Livermore laboratory in California, home of ultra-sophisti-cated research on nuclear weapons and the Starwars programme. At one time it was feared that the virus had infected the Pentagon military com-puters which control missile surveillance and launching. The hacker was Robert T. Morris, a graduate from Cornell university whose father, ironi-cally, was the head scientist at the national computer security centre in Bethesda, Maryland. This branch of the national security agency was dedicated to protecting computers against any exterior threat. Another computer virus which made the headlines was the virus of March 1992, 'created' to celebrate the 517th anniversary of the birth of Michaelangelo.

The myth of the perfect computer

For many years computer manufacturers and their salesmen promoted their product through bluff, never giving a hint that computers might be subject to failure. They gave no instructions on how to deal with break-downs, nor even how to maintain a computer in running order. Further, they failed to emphasise the essential role of the software, although it is the guide and master of the system. Users discovered to their cost that programming a computer takes much more time and money than they had been led to believe.

In his book *Technojolies, Technofolies* on the successful introduction of innovations, Yves Lasfargue includes in a chapter devoted to the society of the future the risks that are increasingly likely to occur. He states that 'we are moving from a society of effort to a society of breakdown' and adds:

> We are now all aware of the technological risks which are spectacular but not commonplace – disasters in chemical factories, major breakdowns in electrical or telephonic networks, rocket explosions and nuclear risks – but we tend to underestimate the daily microbreakdowns in systems using advanced technologies.[23]

However, it now appears that the public is beginning to realise the manifold 'microbreakdowns' which cause chaos in everyday life, such as the closed supermarket till or being stuck in the airport instead of flying off on holiday because of a computer breakdown in air control systems.

Experience has shown that when programmers write software there are between thirty and one hundred faults in every thousand lines, a figure which can be reduced to under ten through careful inspection and testing. Of these, about half will be due to errors or omissions in the specification of standards and cannot be revealed by testing; they will remain undetected until the system receives a particular set of data which activates them and causes the system to fail. It is therefore not surprising that NASA fears another catastrophic Space Shuttle accident within the next decade – the risk is assessed at 1 in 78 launches into orbit – for the shuttle has no less than 25,600,000 program lines. These codes required the equivalent of 22,096 man-years of work, at a cost of $1,200m.

Software in need of a Red Adair

Software accidents have become so frequent and so dramatic, in financial terms, that a group of specialists has been set up in the USA to fly immediately to the site of any disaster and get the failed computers running again. The director of this team, James A. Wilburn, sees himself as the Red Adair of the computer world.

Some of the more recent disasters are the result of introducing new software into old systems, similar to a heart transplant where the problem lies not in the heart itself but in avoiding rejection of the implant. Sun Microsystems Inc. learned this lesson recently when a new system, designed to process salesmen's orders automatically, totally disrupted the

---

[23] Lasfargue, op. cit., p. 126.

assembly line. As a result the Californian company which had been in profit since 1982 suddenly found itself in the red; and the Bank America Corporation has suffered twice in recent years, at a total cost of $100m.

Irreversible decline

For all these reasons it is no surprise that the computer industry is in crisis and that investment in hardware and software is declining. As indicated earlier in this chapter, the turning-point came in 1983.

Wall Street was quick to react: shares fell and investment in the industry would never be the same. The bloom had faded from computers. This was particularly true of the home computer sector, where prices were cut severely; Texas Instruments abandoned the struggle after an orgy of price cutting which took its 99–4A computer from $1,000 to $49.

Silicon Valley, which had become one of the wonders of the world sheltering the 'little geniuses' who were creating the world of tomorrow, laid off more and more staff. It was no longer the Californian dream. The supply of venture capital dried up, and office rents dropped as tenants moved out. This slow-down proved a rude shock for an industry that had always believed in a boundless future; executives began to realise that the good old days were truly over.

In 1985 it was the UK's turn to discover the deep crisis in the computer industry. Acorn, a specialist in educational hardware and software, was rescued by the Italian firm Olivetti and, from 193p in 1984, Acorn shares fell to 28p in the second week of February 1985. The City got the message, and began to distrust the high-tech world. Clive Sinclair, who had made the headlines for so long, gradually disappeared from the front-page news items; and, as the French news magazine *L'Express* wrote in April 1985, 'God save the computer'.

By the end of the decade computer companies only made the front page in the financial newspapers, and only with announcements of losses. The *Financial Times* of 17 August 1989 carried the headline: 'Wang suspends payments to certain suppliers while negotiations waver', and on the same day a *Wall Street Journal* headline proclaimed: 'Against all expectations, Wang rejects the agreement proposed to restructure its debt.' Two days later the *Financial Times* headed an article, 'SD-Scicon losses exceed £1m'. On 11 September the *Wall Street Journal* said that 'Europe's electronic industry wonders who's next, as Plessey loses fight'. The following week the same journal commented on the slow down in Digital Equipment Corporation which could no longer afford:

> the 1987 extravaganza on Boston's water-front, $26m fête that drew 55,000 people and turned the majestic *Queen Elizabeth II* and the cruiser ship *Oceanic* into floating hotels. Today Digital is nearly dead in the water.

The 1990s have not brought any revival in the computer industry – on the contrary, its overall commercial and financial position has continued to decline, with both profit margins and pay-rolls shrinking. In France, Thomson–France was even forced to close down its computer section on 1 January 1990. The Bull computer corporation hit the front page when, in her first public speech, Prime Minister Edith Cresson criticised the Japanese company NEC for wishing to negotiate a larger share in this capital-starved business. Elsewhere in the western world there were agreements between MIT, Wang and Siemens–Nixdort, and extraordinary bargainings between the two traditional enemies, MIT and Apple. That the all-powerful multinational MIT should feel the need to join forces with Apple and that Apple should agree to negotiate illustrates the depth of the crisis afflicting the computer world.

The exception – the Minitel

In this world of a collapsing IT industry there remains one commercial and popular success, the French domestic videotelephone system known as Minitel. This has proved extremely profitable for the French government, which took the initiative of supplying the screens free of charge to subscribers.

The subscriber can: keep up to date with the news; consult a horoscope; pay bills; reserve a plane or train ticket; buy groceries and have them delivered; have a letter translated and keep in touch with friends throughout the country through the electronic mailbox; play chess; send a complaint to the town hall. Children can use the Minitel to play games, leaving their parents with enormous telephone bills – to the extent that there is a flourishing business selling security cupboards in which to lock up the Minitel. But what the telecommunications industry had not foreseen – because the Minitel was originally designed for professional use – was the 'messagerie rose' – in France 'rose', or pink, refers to soft-core pornography. The user, protected by a pseudonym, contacts others for conversation which may move from the friendly to the openly seductive. Some may exchange telephone numbers and, more rarely, may meet.

> One woman, incensed at the idea that her husband might be sending flirtatious messages to other women while she was sitting in the same room, logged on to a friend's Minitel with a suggestive pseudonym. She was soon overwhelmed with racy propositions, including one from her husband. He awoke next day to find his wife gone and the Minitel on the pillow.[24]

---

[24] Justine de Lacy, 'The Sexy Computer', in *Computers in the Human Context*, op. cit. p. 233.

Back to writing

Although the Minitel system has given a certain boost to IT in France, it should not be forgotten that this is only a gadget, that it operates only in France, and that it has not transformed the French way of life. Further, this success cannot conceal the fact that the world's computer industry is only advancing on the technological plateau indicated in the introduction to this work and that it will be sustained there for a while by traditional techniques brought up to date by the latest applications.

One of these techniques is the traditional pen transformed into an electronic pen, enabling the user to write directly on to a special screen which is set on a computer no bigger than a telephone directory. In 1991 it was manufactured by only two companies (GRID and NCR), but others such as Microsoft and Go, in association with IBM, are joining the contest and investing in this old fashioned technology for tomorrow's world.

Another of yesterday's technologies for the future is the fax, or telecopier, another revenge of writing over the audiovisual. 1993 witnessed its 150th anniversary. It was patented on 27 May 1843 by a Scotsman, Alexander Baird. And yet we have had to wait until the end of the twentieth century for the fax to become a revolutionary business tool. Millions of telecopiers transmit typed or handwritten pages in a few seconds every day to the ends of the earth. Why such a surge of activity? Because the fax is a triumph of simplicity: it needs only a telephone socket and a power socket.

Another return to the past, despite the predictions of MacLuhan, is the return of the book, revived by the microedition and the word processor. Who would have thought it, only a few years ago? Certainly not the author of this book. In November 1938 I wrote a report on television in France, convinced that the future belonged to the visual. I was so convinced that I wanted to have a transmitter, at a time when the Eiffel Tower was transmitting on only five days a week between 4 pm and 8 pm. Never later than 8 pm – the engineers refused to work at night ...

By the end of the war I still believed firmly that the audio-visual represented the future and that writing belonged to the past. For several years, therefore, I tried to direct films, and above all I tried not to write books. It was only when I realised that writing was not disappearing that I began to write my first book, *The Cathedral Builders*, published by Editions Seuil in 1958.

CHAPTER 3

Space brought down to Earth

The alternative future which fascinated me just before the Second World War was the conquest of space. With my father, I attended a series of meetings of the first French astronautical society, where scholars and engineers looked at ways of reaching the stars. In his diary for 27 May 1939 my father described our conversation with an engineer, M. Mélot, who was studying rockets to boost the speed of aircraft. He foresaw that before reaching the moon it would first be necessary to travel closer round the Earth:

> For the moment we must be content with working towards the high-powered aircraft that will enable us to leave the earth and make short trips of a few hundred miles into space, returning to earth; we can foresee many difficulties and counterblows, but it is impossible to know how man will be affected when he is no longer subjected to gravity. As it is, we do not do too well upside down. We understand a vacuum and create one, but no amount of calculation brings us to a true knowledge of the effects of an absence of gravity, we have to experiment to find a way to move in such an environment. Twenty years from now will have to elapse before those little excursions which you, M. Gimpel, call the suburbs.[1]

This was a remarkable prediction, for 22 years later, on 12 April 1961, the Soviet Yuri Gagarin undertook the first manned voyage into the 'suburbs' of the Earth.

Mélot was worried about the unknown effects of weightlessness, but he had no remedies to suggest, unlike Kepler who recommended that astronauts should be 'Dazed by opiates'.[2] Today, opiates are routinely used by cosmonauts on space flights. In a report on life aboard a Soviet space craft, Soyuz 29, in 1979, we read that Vladimir Kovalyonak and Alexander Ivanchenko needed drugs.

> Unloading Progress – an orbital and command module – and keeping the systems going occupied much of their time but despite that Kovalyonak and Ivanchenko had difficulty getting to sleep at night

---

[1] René Gimpel, *The Diary of an Art Dealer*, (London, 1991), p. 440.

[2] Koestler, *The Sleepwalkers*, op. cit. p. 422.

and had to resort to drugs. Other problems tended to be minor. Ivanchenko lost weight until supplies of cheese arrived on Progress; he had ear-ache, cured by an alcoholic drink; and both had headaches until they springcleaned the air purifiers.[3]

Physical problems in space flights

Kepler also foresaw what would happen to the limbs of astronauts on a journey into space. On 21 December 1988, when Vladimir Titov and Moussa Manarova returned to earth after 366 days in space, it was found that their muscle fibres had atrophied and their bones were brittle. Both had grown a few centimetres taller and their ankles were 15 per cent smaller.

Since detailed medical studies on the health of cosmonauts are not easily available it is interesting to read about the effects of microgravity on mammals. In October 1987 we learned that after only 12 days in space on a Soviet ship:

> ... the humerus bones of rats became 40 per cent more brittle and the strength of vertebrae in the spinal column decreased by 27 per cent. Fluid accumulated between the muscle fibres of the rats. The mito-chondria in the heart muscle degenerated and skeletal muscles shrank in size. The proportion of helper and suppressor-T cells changed in the blood, thereby weakening the immune system. The levels of cho-lesterol and triglycerides increased while the size of the testes and the magnitude of sperm production decreased.[4]

It is therefore not surprising that some astronauts suffer serious physical strain and have to be brought down to earth prematurely. This hap-pened in February 1982 when the 'commander Yuri Malachev went down with flu and a suspected heart attack'.[5] In the autumn of 1985:

> the new commander of Solyut 7 was noticed by his colleagues to be listless, fatigued, uninterested in his work and to spend long hours simply gazing out of the window. Victor Savinyikh and Alexander Volkov reluctantly reported deteriorating psychological condition to the ground mission control who at once ordered the mission to be ter-minated. The three cosmonauts evacuated the station and parachuted into the snow on November 11. Varyutin was rushed to hospital.[6]

[3] Brian Harvey, Race into Space - the Soviet Space Program, (Chichester, 1988), p. 279.

[4] 'Animals show how microgravity grinds you down', New Scientist, 25 Feb, 1989, p. 26. Ian Anderson

[5] Harvey, Race into Space, op. cit., p. 302.

[6] Ibid., p. 319.

Other cosmonauts such as Valery Vassyutin and Alexander Laveikin have been unable to adapt to the weightlessness of space and have had to be brought down to earth and given medical care.

Even those astronauts who have apparently not suffered from their travels in space are taken to hospital on stretchers, for they cannot stand; on leaving the space capsule they would collapse immediately in a faint if they tried to stand upright. They are treated for days or even weeks in hospital under the constant surveillance of doctors and psychologists.

The death of the astronaut Anatoli Levchenko in August 1988, less than eight months after his mission on the orbital station *Mir*, aroused speculation about the health of other cosmonauts, despite the assertions of doctors who

> were adamant that Levchenko's death was not connected with his space mission, from which post mission reports indicated he had adapted with remarkable ease. The cause of death given in the official obituary as 'a grave illness', has since been attributed to a brain tumour. However, if this tumour was not identified in the rigorous medical checks which Levchenko must have regularly undergone during his almost twenty years as test-pilot and trainee cosmonaut, the question must be asked: do any other cosmonauts in the Soviet space programme have health problems which have gone undetected? This could have considerable implications, not only for the Soviet Mars programme but also for Mir and future orbital stations.[7]

If Levchenko's destination in December had been not *Mir* but Mars, he would have died in mid-mission, thus very possibly causing the failure of the voyage. If Malachev, Vasyutin and Leveikin's goal had also been Mars their failure to adapt to space conditions would have had disastrous consequences.

The planned missions to Mars are still dangerous projects because, as the medical reports show, the general physical condition of all cosmonauts deteriorates seriously after four to six months in space. So when the cosmonauts land on Mars after some eight months or more their physical condition will be poor, at best, and there will be no welcoming medical team to lay them on stretchers and take them to hospital. There will be no rest-home to recover in; they will have to work in an extremely inhospitable environment for weeks or even months, before setting off again in their spacecraft for another wearisome and demanding journey of at least eight months. And that's if all goes well ...

---

[7] 'Doubts over long-term space flight after cosmonaut's death', *Nature*, 18 August 1988.

Americans on Mars ... rather you than me

If all goes well ... yes indeed – for the trials of space travel are even greater than had been thought. When in April 1990 President Bush predicted that within 30 years US astronauts would plant the US flag on Mars he must have been day-dreaming, or had not read what US biomedical experts had discussed only a month earlier in New Orleans at the annual meeting of the AAAS (American Association for the Advancement of Science). Scientists are gradually discovering other ailments which, combined with weightlessness, could seriously hamper long space flights. 'The greatest obstacles arise from cosmic radiation,' said Francis Moore, a professor of surgery at the Harvard medical school, at the AAAS meeting. He went on to say that 'radiation in space can bring increased risk of cancer and cause extremely serious illness if astronauts are insufficiently shielded'. Shielding which is adequate against unexpected events such as solar flares has not yet been designed. 'If an unusual burst of cosmic rays threatens astronauts on the moon they can be brought back,' stated Frank Martin, head of exploration at NASA.

> The real problem, however, is Mars. The fastest trip to Mars would take eight months, each way[8] ... during a solar flare the dose of radiation from high energy particles received by an astronaut outside Earth's orbit could exceed 10 rem in 16 hours. The current limit recommended by the US government is 0.5 rem per year, and 5 rem for workers in nuclear plants.[9]

Shielding astronauts from radiation in deep space remains a problem which is nowhere near being solved.

There was evidence of disquiet over radiation when NASA distributed 12 million tomato seeds which had spent six years in orbit, to 4 million university students. The University of Oklahoma was very surprised:

> In a report it was stressed that the seeds might be toxic and that experiments undertaken on different generations of tomatoes from these samples must be stopped. Certain mutations would appear in the second or third generation. Despite this warning only 6,000 professors returned the suspect seeds to NASA. Others, it was said, thoroughly enjoyed the exquisite flavour of the space tomatoes.[10]

But there are further tribulations confronting travel in space, particularly the wear and tear affecting high-tech equipment – problems which sci-

---

[8] Space may be 'too dangerous' for human beings, a report on the AAAS meeting in New Orleans, *New Scientist*, 3 March 1990.

[9] Ibid.

[10] Albert Ducrocq, 'Tomates suspectes', *Sciences et Avenir*, December 1990, 15.

ence fiction writers and Soviet and NASA planners omitted to take seriously. We are now learning that half of the instruments aboard the MIR were not operational and that instead of concentrating on scientific experiments the team spent most of its time repairing equipment.

The maintenance problems facing a future US space station has become such a major issue that cartoonists make a feature of it in the papers. On 27 March 1990 the scientific review *Nature* printed a cartoon by Birch in which a NASA official interrupts a young would-be astronaut who has been listing his wide knowledge to ask authoritatively, 'That's enough about your qualifications – how are you with a screwdriver?'

The point of the NASA official's concern is obvious when we learn that the outer shield of the space-station will consist of no less than 5,578 panels. It has been estimated that there would be about one failure per day affecting an essential part of this outer shield; and it has been further calculated that maintenance of the station would require at least 2,300 hours per year of space-walking, with a serious potential risk to life and health for the astronauts exposed daily to all kinds of radiation risk, micrometeorites and the thousands of speeding pieces of satellite debris. The same report concluded that the station's construction, expected to take five years, would only be 60–70 per cent complete before the astronauts would have to turn from assembly to undertake an elaborate programme of inspection, preventive maintenance and repair. It is perhaps hardly surprising that the US President Clinton told NASA in 1993 to develop a small space station where the astronaut would need to do less screwdriving.

The failed Phobos mission to Mars

Even when the space station is completed, man will still be a very long way from Mars. The difficulties of reaching Mars were highlighted by the failure of two Soviet probes, *Phobos 1* and *2*, launched in mid-1988 to circle Phobos, a Martian moon, and prepare the way for a manned mission to Mars. In the early 1970s the Soviets launched sixteen spacecraft to Mars; only two reached their objective: the others failed to leave the Earth's atmosphere, encountered various communication problems, missed the planet, or crashed into it. The two spacecraft which did land were unable to transmit data because of a dust storm. It must be recalled that at the same time the more versatile US craft *Marine 29* was able to wait out the storm and to photograph the entire planet from orbit for the first time.

However, for the development of *Phobos 1* and *2* the Soviet Union had had the benefit of the scientific collaboration of a number of powers in both the east and the west, as well as a number of multinational agencies. Yet this did not lead to any better result for these space flights.

Phobos 1 was lost because a computer operator sent the wrong message which made the spacecraft's solar panels turn away from the sun, with the result of a permanent loss of power. Philip Clark, British consultant with Commercial Space Technology, joked over the mistake, suggesting that instead of sending the craft a message saying 'Goodnight and sleep well,' the controller must have said 'Goodnight and kill yourself'. The resulting muddle in the logic circuits of the craft's computers was probably beyond repair even if they were turned on again.

Here we touch on one of the themes of this work: that of human error in computer operation. Science fiction writers have often imagined computers coming to life and taking over control from their masters, but have they taken human error into account? The scientists and engineers who created the world of microchips apparently ignored this basic factor. Our society today is therefore at risk because of the real possibility of human blunder.

Phobos 2 was lost because its main transmitter failed in March 1989, just as it was preparing to get within 15 metres of its namesake Phobos, the Martian moon.

More recently, in August 1993, NASA's Mars observer unaccountably stopped transmitting radio signals to Earth as it was about to enter orbit around the Red Planet. Investigators blamed poor planning for the embarrassing failure of the mission.

The prohibitive cost of space travel

On the heels of the failure of the unmanned Phobos probes came the unexpected announcement that the Soviet Union was to suspend its pioneering manned programme on board the orbiting spacecraft *Mir*. The crew of the *Mir* was recalled to Earth in April 1989 and the craft was left unmanned for the first time since its launch in February 1986. The station was not reoccupied until September 1989, but only after the astronauts had been forced to link up manually after the failure of the automatic docking system.

Several reasons were cited for the recall: technical problems with the station itself and delays in launching add-on sections to expand *Mir*. The truth is, however, that the Soviet space programme was fighting for survival.

The Soviet Union's economic and political restructuring had turned the spotlight on to hitherto hidden areas of public expenditure, including the country's massive space programme. National pride was no longer sufficient justification for expending rare resources on ambitious space projects. The Soviet people wanted consumer goods, not missions to Mars.

In reality, the trials and tribulations of space flight begin down here on our own planet, with very down-to-earth monetary problems. Lack of finance has forced the Soviets to seek sponsors in the UK. For £16m they were prepared to send a British man or woman into space; industry was very slow to respond, however, and the price demanded by the Soviets had to be reduced before Helen Sherman was sent up to their *Mir* station in May 1991. And politics can intervene in a major way. With the break-up of the Soviet Union in August 1991, one of the astronauts, who accompanied Helen Sherman to the station, Sergeev Kouhela, was to stay in space against his will and then at the launching pad at Baikonov, many more months than had been planned. And his tribulations were increased when he was not able to get his ration of honey due to export restrictions into Kazakhstan.

The marooning of Kouhela in space – very science fiction – made the headlines at a time when the image of space was fading. A *New Scientist* poll in 1989 found that only 3 per cent of the population – compared with 17 per cent in 1985 – puts 'space exploration' as the greatest scientific achievement since the Second World War.

> About the same percentage thought that space exploration should receive priority when it comes to handing out money for research, a fall in interest from 5 per cent four years ago. And 38 per cent said that space exploration should have its budget limited or reduced.[11]

A team from the Department of External Studies at the University of Oxford found similar percentages: 43 per cent of those questioned considered that the government was spending too much on exploring space. Only research on weapons for national defence scored higher.

In the USA the proportion of the population hostile to space travel may be slightly lower, although there is nonetheless a general reluctance to 'throw money at the stars'.[12] The sums involved are stupendous. In March 1990 NASA expected the trip to Mars to cost $541,000m over 30 years. Congress may vote the funds one year but not the next, so the project may flounder and we are probably safe in predicting that in the year 2020 there will be no one on Mars. In support of this prediction the reader is advised to read carefully the work of Arthur Mill, *Mars: the Next Step*, in which the author reminds us that in 1969 NASA had predicted that twenty years later, in 1989, there would be 48 men living on Mars on a semi-permanent basis, with 24 others in orbit round the planet. How wrong can one be?

---

[11] 'Space is far out', *New Scientist*, 2 September 1989.
[12] Ibid.

Scientists against manned flights

After unveiling NASA's agency budget for 1994, Daniel Goldin, head of NASA, recognised the difficulties of manned space flights when he stated: 'Technically speaking we are not ready to return to the moon or go to Mars. We have not established that humans can live and work in those extremely hostile environments for long periods of time. We have not done the precursory robotic scouting missions that are necessary.' This statement of facts will reassure the scientific community, which has long considered that manned space expeditions have little scientific justification and that putting man in space is taking money away from basic scientific research 'on the ground'.

On the eve of a symposium on manned space flights, organised in Strasbourg in 1986 by the European Space Agency with the participation of six European astronauts, the space research committee of the French Academy of Science published a strongly-worded report against manned space flights. This stated that:

> The principal justification for these flights envisaged by European nations was to affirm their ability to put man into space with purely European means ... While some observations depend upon sensors in space, these could perfectly well be undertaken from a ground station or automata relaying data. Further, as satellites are often in orbits that are extremely hostile even for the well-protected astronaut the role of man in their maintenance is also questionable.[13]

In terms of cost, it has been estimated that an astronaut's time in space costs roughly $18,000 per hour.

It is therefore perhaps not surprising that on Friday 25 August 1989 astronomers of the world celebrated one of the great technological and scientific feats in history, when the US spacecraft *Voyager 22* sent back spectacular photographs of the most distant planet in the solar system, Neptune. This was achieved after 12 years of flight, covering some 7 million kilometres round the giant planet discovered by Galileo in 1612 which revolves round the sun not in 365 days but in 160 years. This remarkable voyage was of course achieved by an unmanned spacecraft: no man could ever have survived such a voyage through the solar system. The total cost of the operation was only $865m, a fraction of the cost of the proposed space station or a manned mission to Mars. And although *Voyager's* main radio receiver had failed and its radar scanner had suffered a few lubrication problems, all its instruments for scientific measurement had functioned correctly. They were the high-tech equip-

---

[13] '"Non" to man in space', *Nature*, 5 May 1990.

ment of the 1970s. Today's high-tech computers are so much more sophisticated that the risk of breakdown is considerably greater.

What are we getting from deep space?

However exceptional the encounter of *Voyager II* with Neptune and its moon Triton, it would certainly not have made the newspaper headlines if it had not occurred during the summer when news is scarce. The *New Scientist* noted the lack of public interest in major events in space.

> The spacecraft may have arrived within minutes of its scheduled time, but it would be taking conspiracy theory, or good timing, too far to suggest that NASA planned this PR coup. However, NASA must be immensely grateful for this opportunity to breathe life back into the flagging venture that is science in space. Space certainly needs something to revive its fading image.[14]

If only the spacecraft which have approached and photographed all the planets save Pluto had found signs of life, we would be so much more interested and excited; but none of the probes despatched to distant planets have found any trace of the existence of an ET (extra-terrestrial). We have constructed powerful radio receivers and listened to thousands of ever-silent stars, we have even sent our own signals to unresponsive planets. It is all very disappointing. If the slightest trace of an ET had been found it would have justified the money spent, and more. As the Italian scientist Enrico Fermi enquired, in 1939, long before the search for Extra-terrestrial Intelligence began, 'Where are the Extra-Terrestrials? Why haven't they landed in their flying saucers on the lawn of the White House to welcome mankind to the Galactic Club?'

However some astronomers, like Victor Shvartsman, an astronomer of the Special Astrophysical Observatory in the Caucasus – the site of the world's most powerful optical telescope – are entirely undaunted by the fact that almost thirty years of searching for radio signals from other civilisations have drawn a blank. The problem, he believes, is that we concentrate our efforts on looking for the wrong kind of signal. Research is now based on laser signals.

A recently founded discipline, bioastronomy, is concentrating on searching for extra-terrestrial life and intelligence. Some of its members 'are living in a quasi-messianic state of mind, awaiting an ET contact'.[15] But the US Congress voted in September 1993 to discontinue NASA's 'Search for Extra-Terrestrial Intelligence' project.

---

[14] 'Space is far out', loc. cit.

[15] Emmanuel Davoust, 'La recherche de la vie extra-terrestre', *La Recherche*, 211 (1988).

What can we expect from the suburbs of Earth?

Although experts had predicted that the 1990s would see the pharmaceuticals industry in particular devoting millions of dollars to manufacturing products in weightless conditions, such developments now seem entirely hypothetical. Virtually no one still expects commercial production of drugs or computer chips in space until well into the next century.

In the mid 1980s, when McDonnell Douglas and the Ortho pharmaceuticals division of Johnson & Johnson conducted successful experiments on the shuttle *Discovery*, in particular the production of a hormone suitable for developing new drugs, experts expected a rush of similar ventures. Today, McDonnell Douglas and Ortho have given up this project in favour of old-fashioned laboratory bench work. Much the same is true of gallium arsenide, a substance used to replace sillicium in electronic computer chips.

Reimar Lust, Director-General of the European Space Agency since 1984, stated in an interview:

> The first thing to understand is that there is little chance of gaining a quick economic return from space science and technology. To promise otherwise is to misrepresent your aims to the public ... industry normally thinks of getting a return on its investment in a time of six or seven years. In space the return may be after thirty years.[16]

Remote observation, for example, will not become commercially viable in the near future. Furthermore, the US remote sensing satellite LANDSAT, which cost near to $200m, has been floating uselessly in an unknown orbit since October 1993, while EOSAT – the Earth Observation Satellite Company – which processes and markets the information, banked only $18m in 1988. It is therefore not surprising that EOSAT talked to their French counterparts about merging the two nations' remote-observation programmes in the mid-1990s – particularly as Spot Image, the company set up by the CNRS (the state research centre) to market Spot pictures is still far from profitability. In 1987 its turnover was FF130m, while in 1988 overheads were running at FF210m. And Spot 2 is estimated to have cost FF500m to build.

To attract attention to the scientific benefits to be derived from space, some agencies exploiting satellite information such as METEOSAT or ARGOS were giving their data virtually free to oceanographers, vulcanologists and other specialists. Henceforward, however, a more realistic price will have to be paid – which few scientific institutions will be able to afford.

---

[16] 'Reimar Lust on Europe's space plans', *The Scientist*, 11 January 1988.

Forward into the past, or the limits of technology

The power failure which crippled India's $140m multifunction INSAT–IC satellite a week after its *Ariane* rocket launch in July 1988 came as a blow to the Indian space research organisation. This set-back added to the already growing uncertainty in the international commercial satellite market and encouraged both manufacturers and users to look again at earth-based communication systems. Telephone companies are reducing their dependence on satellites by turning to ground-based fibre optics transmission systems.

Again and again we will come across this phenomenon of upgrading techniques which appear to be obsolete. While the US was focussing on the shuttle, a high-tech white elephant, the USSR was concentrating very successfully on improving an earlier technique, the rocket, which enabled them to overtake the USA in the space race. They even built a super booster, the *Energyiya* rocket, capable of launching 100 tonnes into space. The Europeans, with the French *Ariane* rocket, have captured more than half of the commercial satellite market. The Americans in turn appear to be responding to nostalgia for past days and are preparing to revive Saturn 5, which launched the Apollo missions to the moon. More remarkable still is the NASA project to withdraw the antiquated Skylab from the National Space Museum in Washington DC and relaunch it into space.

When the Soviets had the unfortunate idea of turning to high-tech, the financial consequences were commensurately great. This happened with the construction of the space shuttle *Buran*, on the model of the US shuttle. The former director of the Moscow space research institute stated that technologically it was a dazzling success, but financially a costly mistake. In June 1993, Russia's space shuttle was finally grounded. The planned flight of the *Buran* shuttle to the *Mir* station in 1994 will not now take place. The USA acknowledged officially that the cost of space shuttles was wholly unreasonable and, through Vice President Dan Quayle, announced in July 1991 that they would finance no more of them. The four shuttles currently in use will continue to fly special missions until the next century.

In defence of the shuttle we should accept the fact – not always recognised in our industrial and scientific society – that technology, whether advanced or traditional, is and always will be less than perfect. In an article in the *New York Times*, 'Overarmed Earth could go the way of *Challenger*', Adèle Simmons and John Sanbonmatsu observed, concerning the Star Wars strategic defence programme:

> The fault – which caused the 1986 *Challenger* catastrophe – does not lie

in American technology but in the nature of technology itself. We are so used to our machines functioning correctly that when they go wrong we are invariably surprised, sometimes angry. But go wrong they will, inevitably. Hoping to build a 'perfect' machine – one that will always work the way it is supposed to – is as unrealistic as hoping to build a perpetual machine. The first defies human capacity for perfectibility, the second defies the laws of physics. Machines are mortal because we are mortal.[17]

An illustration of high-tech is the explosion of the *Ariane 4* rocket in February 1990, caused by a discarded soiled rag. This cost Ariane Space $36–54m and delayed future launches. The loss of the two Japanese communication rockets carried by the ill-fated rocket may harm Japan's efforts to promote its daily high-definition television transmissions. The project had already suffered a mishap in space caused by the failure of the first satellite created for broadcasting, BS–2A, with a malfunction of its transponder.

The month after this mishap the Americans had two of their own. A spy satellite exploded and left the $150m communication satellite *Intelsat* stranded in a low elliptical orbit waiting for a rescue which may never come. The *Hipparchos* astronomy observation satellite, launched in 1989, became trapped in 1990 in an elliptical orbit rather than in its intended geo-stationary orbit. The most spectacular set-back, however, occurred in the *Hubble* space telescope which cost $1.5–2.5m to construct and launch in April 1990. Its main mirror was the victim of a manufacturing fault: to general horror and amazement, it was discovered that the telescope was short-sighted, suffering from flickering and forgetfulness. A computer remedy had to be developed on earth which would reduce the blur of the pictures it was sending back. This was disappointing. The repair to the *Hubble* space telescope was spectacularly successful, but the repair mission cost $b30m–1.2bn.

Back to bread and circuses

At a less elevated level, what may turn out to be a financial bonanza or possibly a financial flop are the telecommunications satellites – at least for those which survive the trauma of their launch and which beam entertainment programmes into millions of European homes. The standard of the programmes is reminiscent of the circus games offered to the Roman populace. The UK can tune in to the *Disney Channel* for 18 hours a day, to *Lifestyle* with programmes consisting of televised games, soap

---

[17] Adèle Simons is President of Hampshire College. John Sanbonmatsu is Assistant to the Director of the Five Colleges Program for Peace and World Security. Article republished in the *International Herald Tribune*, 10 February 1988.

operas and chat shows, to *MTV Europe* with its round-the-clock pop music presented by young video jockeys, to *Super Channel* to watch old classics such as Benny Hill, *Dr Who*, and *Dempsey and Makepeace*, or *Eurosport* for specialised sports programmes, etc.

But this is where the merry-go-round must stop, for there will never be enough TV viewers to make television advertising profitable on all our screens. A European household watches on average little more than two hours per day, less than a third of the US equivalent. And how many households are going to buy the dishes and decoders to receive these programmes when the European satellite stations will soon be operating on three different frequency bands, using at least six incompatible transmission systems? The potential purchaser is faced with a bewildering array of choices. What size dish? How many satellites, and which ones? Which channel to watch and which to subscribe to? How many decoder boxes to pile up in the living room? Even the professionals acknowledge the muddle. An advertisement in the June 1989 issue of the journal *What Satellite?* read: 'With the future of Satellite very much in the air, it pays to have your feet firmly on the ground.' In 1994 the competition for viewers has never been tougher. 'TV wars are breaking out, cut-throat competition is taking place in an industry that saw viewing grow by only 4 per cent in 1993, while the channel choice multiplied enormously.'[18] The problem is one of revenue: the channels depend on advertising for their income and advertisers need ratings. The new channels are spreading their ratings very thin.

In October 1990 the two British satellite channels, Sky and BSB, came together as BSkyB to limit their financial losses. This was a thunderclap in the televisual sky, but it was a response to economic reality. The fusion, however, meant rejection in the UK for a high-tech system which the European Community sought to impose, high-definition television – HD Mac – and the endorsement of an old form of technology, the PAL. France too has her satellite problems.

In 1988 *Ariane 1* successfully launched the French telecommunications satellite TDF–1, designed to transmit high definition images with digital stereo – TVHD – to households throughout the whole of Europe, provided they have access to the right kind of parabolic antenna which can cost between £400 and £800 to purchase and instal. The TDF–1 Satellite is a twin to the failed TV–Sat 1 which was launched by West Germany the previous year and which had to be written off as a loss after one of its 60-foot solar panels failed to extend, thus blocking the signal relay.

Some critics have implied that TDF–1 may perhaps be the space equivalent of Concorde or the Superphoenix, a technological marvel with no prospect of commercial viability. Whatever the sums paid by subscribers

---

[18] *What Satellite TV*, March 1994, p. 12.

to the channels, they will never cover the capital investment. Further, the government was forced to invest in a second satellite, TDF–2, to cover any risk of malfunction and premature withdrawal of TDF–1. These two satellites have cost the French government – in other words the taxpayer – some FF4bn. Today, both satellites are incapacitated and:

> They revolve round the planet without programmes, without audience. Without a future, too: no one trusts them since they lost one-third of their transmission tubes ... for ten years a few Cassandra figures have made as much noise as they can ... now the whole of the little audiovisual world is wondering how to repair the damage and save what can still be saved.[19]

For various reasons, the fact remains that satellites have currently a limited future. The forecasts of the early 1980s are not coming true. Ariane Space is the most reliable launcher, but the sixty-third flight of an Ariane rocket crashed into the Atlantic late in January 1994 with two satellites insured for £235m. This will hinder Ariane Space's ambitions to launch ten or more satellites a year. This tendency towards fewer satellite launches lends weight to my arguments concerning the limits and levelling out of advanced technologies.

---

[19] Claude Soulat, TDF-1/TDF-2: 'Les monstres de l'espace', *L'Obs Economie*, 3–9 January 1991, p. 45.

4

Back to the Balloon

As more satellites break down and their costs soar out of sight, scientists are turning back to the humble balloon, a form of technology little changed since its invention two centuries ago but now brought up to date for specialised missions. These may include exploring the origins of matter or of the universe. At the National Scientific Center in Texas, balloons bigger than a football field can lift two tonnes or more of scientific equipment up to a height of 50 kilometres. These instruments can help to determine the original nature of the universe and how matter has evolved since then.

Balloons are not only cheaper than satellites, they take less time to construct and are easier to recover in the event of failure or for routine maintenance.

Back to airships

Airships, long regarded as the dinosaurs of aviation, are back in favour. Revitalised through high-tech, they are flying silently over the great cities once more, their monitoring causing no disturbance. An airship equipped with ultra-sophisticated electronic surveillance systems flew over Paris and the Bastille during the ceremonies commemorating the bicentenary of the French Revolution, ready to give warning of any terrorist attack against the seven heads of state from the most highly industrialised nations assembled for the celebrations.

The British firm Westinghouse–Airship Industries has signed a multi-million dollar contract with the US navy to build an enormous new airship to protect the USA against cruise missiles. It will combine some of the most useful surveillance features of satellites, aircraft and surface ships and, because it is made very largely of non-metallic materials, it will be almost invisible to enemy radar. Its own antenna, mounted inside the gas envelope, will be capable of giving timely warning of the approach of any bombers or supersonic missiles.

Realising that this was a way to survey 20–30 times as large an area as ground-based engineers could cover, Australian scientists are using an airship as a giant metal detector; this is particularly cost-effective in vast expanses of trackless and otherwise inaccessible terrain, unsuitable for aircraft to land.

The French architect and poet Gilles Ebersolt has found a revolution-ary use for the lighter-than-air craft, using first a Montgolfier hot air bal-loon and later an airship as a raft for 'landing' on tree tops. Professor Francis Hall, of the Botanical Institute at the University of Montpellier II perceived the scientific benefits of using a canopy raft – an ultra-light structure consisting of inflatable 'sausages' linked together by a net – to study the flora of the Amazonian rain forest, hitherto little explored because of its inaccessibility.

All previous means of access such as trunk climbing, observation tow-ers, aerial walkways or aerial photography, share the same problems: they offer access and study of only certain species of tree and it is impos-sible to obtain samples of statistical significance or carry out team obser-vation.

The question arises: why use hot-air balloons or airships when heli-copters are available? The answer is simple – the helicopter rotor-blades tend to damage the tree-tops and the noise and wind created by the rotors destroy the very flowers and insects that the botanists have come to study.

The Earth-bound helicopter industry

Unfortunately helicopters have a very restricted life and range of activity in our present-day world; it could be said that they have never really taken off. On 1 January 1991 France had only 750 helicopters, exactly the same number as the UK. Throughout the whole world there are only some 16,000 civilian helicopters, although there are hundreds of millions of cars. At the same date a mere ninety-two private individuals owned their own helicopter. It is in fact a craft industry, a clear expression of the limitations of our industrial civilisation.

But why has this form of transport suffered such restricted develop-ment? Some people may at first perhaps feel a certain apprehension over riding in a helicopter; there is the noise of the rotors; in recent years ecol-ogists have lost no opportunity for banning flights over cities by these 'devilish machines' and there is the cost of aviation fuel – the Sikorsky S.76 consumes 340 litres per hour. The greatest cost, however, remains that of maintenance, for obvious safety reasons. It is therefore hardly sur-prising that in its reply to a young reader who enquired what was required to become a pilot, the magazine Science et Vie junior stated that 'the cost of an hour of helico flight is £250 minimum'.[1] In the USA one of the last city helicopter services, linking Boston airport with its suburbs, ceased operating in 1991.

---

[1] 'Cher hélicoptère', Science et vie junior, May 1991, 10.

Restrictions on helicopter flights are so severe that one of the world's largest conurbations, London, has only one heliport, Westland. Even this is threatened with closure by local authorities. Some of the problems of this advanced technology can be better understood with knowledge of the regulations imposed on the heliport and on flight restrictions over London. Under the terms of its licence the heliport can only be used when weather conditions permit: by day, horizontal visibility of one kilometre and cloud base of 600 feet are the minimum requirements, while at night these change to three kilometres and a cloud base of 1,000 feet. And whenever helicopters enter the city's air zone they must remain strictly 'clear of clouds and be visible from the ground or water'.

Access to the heliport along air corridors is limited in terms of numbers and, in most cases, hours. The routes must be capable of being followed on the ground. Between Barnes, however, to the west of the heliport, and London Bridge to the east, and towards Greenwich, helicopters are forced to follow the route of the river Thames.

Such restrictions go a long way to explain why the only scheduled flights in the UK are those operated by British International Helicopters between Penzance and the Isles of Scilly; flights which take place, of course, over the sea.

In the 1970s I took a helicopter flight from John F. Kennedy airport to the roof of the Pan Am building on Park Avenue. Such flights were regular at that time, but were halted after a near-accident on the landing site of the Pan Am skyscraper.

Supersonic flights grounded

Although Concorde still flies between the USA and Europe, it no longer operates to South America, Africa, Australia or Japan. When the Concordes cease flying, some time between 2005 and 2020, the prestigious Franco–British project will turn out to have been the greatest white elephant in aviation history. It has been a commercial failure for several reasons: first, the sonic boom meant that it could not fly at supersonic speeds over land; secondly, its fuel consumption is very high, its range is limited, and its payload is restricted to one hundred passengers.

To cover Concorde's running costs Air France and British Airways have resorted to operating the supersonic aircraft as a gimmick for the Yuppies, offering them half-hour flights over the Atlantic, or round-the-world flights for rich tourists. But the package holiday to end them all must surely have been the Concorde flight to Lapland in October 1988: passengers left Heathrow on the most advanced passenger aircraft in the world for a rendezvous with Father Christmas. It is years since the last Concorde came off the production line and those airline executives who still advocate supersonic passenger travel seem no more realistic than

Father Christmas himself.

As long ago as 1971 the US Congress refused to allocate funds for the US supersonic craft, the SST, realising no doubt that the US Concorde would be a financial black hole. This `anti-technology' vote represented a complete reversal of the traditional US attitude towards technology. 1971 may come to be seen as the year when western technological civilisation, the inventor of the notion of progress, began to lose faith in the future.

However, this general loss of faith in the future does not seem to have inhibited certain aerospace engineers, who are planning supersonic planes flying at five times the speed of sound. There are newspaper headlines that `Great Britain plans the son of Concorde' or 'Around the World in Sixty Minutes'. The most widely discussed project was Hotol; but the UK government refuses to consider funding for another commercially disastrous supersonic aircraft.

There are rumours of another supersonic project, the Hermes – although there is a certain reticence on the part of some of the potential chief collaborators. Technological problems are still far from resolution and the ecologists are, as ever, on the watch.

Back to the propeller

While some aerospace engineers have been designing costly supersonic craft which will probably never fly, others have been looking to the past to build extremely effective and 'revolutionary' engines – the technology which enabled the Wright brothers to make their historic flight in 1903 – the propeller aircraft.

Modern propeller craft have extraordinary sickle-shaped blades at the back of the engine instead of at the front. There are two sets of eight blades rotating in opposition, the propellers driven by a pair of turbines working in opposite directions. These 'prop fans', as they are known, are already flying with fuel savings of 25–40 per cent when compared with current jet engines. Russian engineers as well as their western counterparts are interested in these techniques.

Back to the river bus

The new London City Airport in London's Docklands, built to bring international financial magnates swiftly into the City, required the reestablishment of the capital's oldest route, the River Thames. A high-speed catamaran takes the passengers to the airport from piers at Chelsea Harbour on a spectacular trip down the Thames. All this because of the risks of delay in traffic jams.

Aerial traffic jams are much more serious, and increasingly frequent, with aircraft queuing up over the world's largest airports as they await authorisation to land. The runways are congested, causing delays in take-off. Every summer in the UK the media proclaim the plight of travellers herded into airport waiting lounges; yet underlying this apparent chaos is the real story concerning the aircraft industry, which is that it has not developed as the prophets of the future had predicted.

Today many people complain that the skies appear to be full of aircraft – but compared with the future as envisaged by the late nineteenth-century French futurologist Robida, the sky is almost completely empty. He very wittily drew a Paris skyline filled with private airships and a lady assaulted by ruffians with a flying police team chasing them high above the city.

How Robida would have laughed if he had seen the great commotion produced in Paris in the summer of 1988 by a small private plane flying over the capital by night. As with most western cities, night flights over Paris are strictly forbidden; the police and the Ministry of Defence used their most sophisticated equipment in vain in their efforts to catch the culprit. It was subsequently discovered that the pilot was the man who a few years previously had flown up the Champs-Elysées and under the arches of the Arc de Triomphe.

Flight restrictions are, as noted above, the main reason for the small number of helicopters, and are probably also the reason for the very limited number of private planes. After the Second World war, convinced that there would be fewer and fewer cars and that we would all soon be airborne, I learned how to fly; but after a few lessons, when I realised how strict the regulations were, I abandoned the idea. A pilot's licence seemed to me to be of no use at all.

Liability laws ground small aircraft

The innumerable curbs on flying small private aircraft no doubt go a long way to explain why there are only 6,000 in France and some 20,000 for the whole of Europe. The figures for the USA are considerably greater – around 230,000 – but the number may have peaked as new restrictions come into force, with serious implications even if they are not directly aimed at this area of transport. The very strict laws relating to civil liability, or tort, are fruitful soil for the growth of legal fortunes, as lawyers defend the aircraft construction companies every time there is an accident – even when pilot error is obvious. For this reason insurance premiums are rising rapidly, with a consequent reduction in the number of new purchases. In the US, premiums have recently reached the point where they represent no less than one third of the price of a private plane.[2]

---

[2] Huber, *Liability - The Legal Revolution*, op. cit., p. 3.

It is therefore not surprising that 'in America manufacturers of small aircraft claim that unlimited legal liability for defects in their products has brought their industry close to collapse'.[3]

Companies like Beech, Cessna and Piper have curtailed or suspended production; they have quickly discovered that the new model planes carrying a 50 per cent surcharge for liability insurance could no longer compete with used planes already on the market.[4] Again because of the insurance cost it is no longer possible to buy a set of construction plans for new planes from Burt Rustan, the pioneer designer of the *Voyager*.[5]

Europe, however, lacks such rigid laws and no similar business has had to close down for this reason. One company in the UK is actually advertising DIY aircraft.

Jetliner industry in retreat

Not only are the manufacturers of small aircraft suffering from a lack of firm orders, the manufacturers of the great jet airliners, airbus industries and Boeing have seen orders being cancelled or postponed. 1993 will be remembered by the industry as an accursed year. The major reason for the decline in orders is the present employment crisis. In the last few years the projected annual increase in airline passengers has turned into a dramatic decrease.

The airlines world-wide have evidently suffered too; in 1993 they experienced a loss of no less than \$4.8bn. To attract passengers, airlines offer reduced prices and lavish advantages. With Lufthansa: 'members can quickly accrue miles for free flights, free hotels and car rental days as well as "Fantasy Awards" like a BMW driver training or piloting a flight in a simulator.' United Airlines recommends passengers to: 'Join Mileage Plan and get a bonus of 5,000 miles into the bargain.' The competition is so fierce that when Air Europe went out of business in 1991, its former chairman, Henry Goodman, commenced a legal action against British Airways for an alleged 'dirty tricks' campaign.

Back to the train

The world crisis is certainly primarily responsible for curbing yearning to fly, but there are other considerations which make passengers hesitate, such as congestion and delay at airports. In the USA incidents in flight

---

[3] *The Economist*, 20 August 1988.

[4] Huber, *Liability - The Legal Revolution*, op. cit., p. 161.

[5] Ibid., p. 4.

or on landing have persuaded passengers to abandon the airplane as a mode of transport. Some pilots have even landed at the wrong airport or on the wrong runway. These errors have become so commonplace that travellers traditionally faithful to air transport are returning to road transport such as the famous Greyhound bus company, an organisation enjoying growing numbers of passengers and therefore of profits.

Americans are also turning back to the railways, which at one time had practically collapsed. They are being wooed away from the airlines with lower prices, films on long hauls and even linen and fine china in the dining cars. Food service on the trains has improved considerably.

> Passengers on a recent trip between Chicago and Denver cited other sound reasons for taking the train, including apprehension about flying in the aftermath of several incidents in which pieces of the aircraft dropped off in flight.[6]

The triumphant rebirth of the train in the USA was confirmed with the signature in May 1991 of a $6bn contract for the construction of a specialised high-speed train similar to the French TGV, to link the route Dallas–Houston–Austin–San Antonio. This will be the continent's first high-speed train. The impetus for this development lies in the tornadoes which paralyse air traffic in this region, and the half-hour waits at the end of the over-crowded runways at Dallas and Houston.

In France passengers increasingly take the TGV not because of the hazards of flying but because it offers a faster and cheaper inter-city service than Air-Inter; the internal airline has lost 60 per cent of its clientele on the Paris–Lyon route, for example. It faces further losses with the opening of the Atlantic TGV between Paris, Poitiers, Angoulême, Bordeaux, Hendaye and Irun. The Atlantic TGV has reached a speed of 515 kmh. What irony, that the Air-Inter management are now afraid of competition from the nineteenth-century technology of railways whereas, like manufacturing industry, their traditional fear has been concentrated on competition from forward-looking high-tech developments! A real turn-round. Air-Inter is now on the defensive and proclaims proudly that it offers a 55-minute flight between Paris and Nantes.

Railways have a further advantage over airlines, since the main terminals are in city centres; air passengers land some distance out from the centre and must make the transfer by road or rail, with all the further waiting and congestion which that involves.

By the mid-1990s the airlines flying the Paris–London route will be faced with even greater competition from the Eurostar trains which should link the two capitals in a little over three hours, through the Channel Tunnel. Albert Mathieu's 1802 designs for a tunnel for coaches

---

6 'Amtrak strains to get all aboard', *International Herald Tribune*, 14 March 1989.

have survived, showing tall ventilation shafts along the length of the route; although few people have remarked on it, today's project shows very little advance over his plan. The boring machines used today are direct descendants of the tunnelling machinery invented by Marc Brunel for the Thames tunnel of the 1830s; and the new Channel Tunnel will not carry a motorway equipped with some revolutionary ventilation system, nor the pneumatic railway discussed at length in the 1970s for a link between New York and Washington, but simply traditional diesel-powered locomotives.

France is not alone, however, in modernising her railway network. The Spanish government has decided to convert its 7,200 miles of railway to the narrower standard European gauge. High speed trains will cover the whole of Europe: Brussels, capital of the European Community, will be only 80 minutes away from Paris. The Barcelona–Paris journey will take 4 hours, London–Cologne just a little more. Lyon and Turin will be virtual neighbours, while the Scots will be able to board a train in Edinburgh after tea and be skiing in the Alps bright and early next morning.

In July 1989 the international news magazine *Newsweek* came out with a front page cover, 'Super-Trains. How they will change the geography of Europe. Clear the track – here comes the super train revolution as radical as the birth of civilian jet liners'. The author of the article, well aware of the influence on future air traffic, wrote:

> ... airlines will almost certainly be the losers. European rail traffic will quadruple between now and 2015 and short haul European carriers are expected to lose as much as half their current business.[7]

It is not only in Europe that new tracks are being built; they are appearing in the former Soviet Union, in China and in Japan, where their high speed Bullet train leaves Tokyo every six minutes.

For many years Japan and Germany have been testing trains which would revolutionise rail travel still further, using trains without wheels moving on cushions of air by magnetic levitation. In March 1994 the German Cabinet gave final approval for the Transrapid which will go into operation in about ten years.

Back to the tram

At a more modest level, rails are being laid in cities once more in order to revive trams. Grenoble built a new tramway in 1981 and Nantes in 1985, while in Paris it was decided in 1983 that this form of transport – banished for over half a century – should be reintroduced in 1992 between

---

[7] Megan Dissly, *Newsweek*, 31 July 1989

the Saint-Denis station and the Bobigny prefecture some ten kilometres away. The average speed will be around 19 km/h, compared with the average Paris bus which at peak times travels at only about 10 km/h. Trams returned to Manchester in March 1992, after an absence of more than 40 years. It is the first new tramway in the UK since before the Second World War. The new £130m Metrolink scheme involves modernising two commuter railway lines and connecting them through the centre of Manchester. The vehicles, which can be coupled together and used as trains, have a top speed of 80 kilometres per hour, but will not exceed 50 km/h in the city centre.

Not only are trams relatively fast, punctual and comfortable, but they have the great advantage of not adding to pollution and ecological damage, a great advantage in modern times. Further, they are very much cheaper to construct than an underground rail line. Strasbourg, for example, has decided against constructing its long-awaited underground system and is now planning a tramway for 1994.

In fact trams have never been entirely abandoned. Many cities across the world still have them, such as Philadelphia and, of course, San Francisco. In Italy, Turin has its trams and there are plans to reintroduce them in other cities.

Back to the bicycle

In London it is perfectly possible to beat the average traffic speed of 11 miles per hour by going to work on a bicycle. This is the chosen transport of many managers, magistrates, civil servants, members of Parliament, ministers ...

> The government recognises the value of bicycles in one way. It pays civil servants 4.7 pence per mile to use them on official business.[8]

The number of bicycles has increased in the UK from 7 million in 1977 to more than 13 million in 1989, but it is in the USA that the use of bicycles has really boomed. In 1985 sales reached 11.4 million, a record second only to the 15.2 million sold in 1973, when Americans were looking for ways to beat the high cost of petrol. Many of these bicycles are sold to commuters, but they are also bought in great numbers for health reasons, particularly by the elderly. Some 78 million Americans ride a bicycle at least once a month; this makes cycling almost the leading form of leisure activity, second only to swimming.

France too is seeing a renewal of interest in outings for sport, rural expeditions, or simply a need for fresh air.

---

[8] 'Free Wheeling', *The Economist*, 25 February 1989.

Today there is a steadily increasing public enthusiasm for cycling, with numbers doubling in two years and nearly 3 million bicycles sold in 1990.[9]

'New materials, incorporation of aerodynamic factors ... there has been more technical progress in bicycles in the last five years than at any other time since they were invented':[10] metal streamlining, development of steel-chrome molybdenum alloys, wind-tunnel studies. The Michelin company has developed a new generation of virtually puncture-proof tyres. The result of all this research is a new type of bicycle, the mountain bike, with a sturdy frame, broad tyres with heavy tread, and small wheels. This opens up cycling through woodlands, up hillsides and across gravel. Slopes of 15 per cent no longer frighten the Sunday cyclist; with a little fitness training anyone can bicycle up 30–40 per cent hills, and 24-speed gear changes provide almost infinite adaptation to the terrain. Annual sales of mountain bikes of nearly one million are now one-third of the French market.

Back to sailing

No less surprising in the transport world is the return of the sail to the high seas, in a completely new form. In 1984 the Japanese launched a 31,000 tonne freighter with rigid vinyl chloride and polyester sails, their angle controlled automatically by computer. Sails add auxiliary power to the ship's conventional engines.

The following year France's celebrated explorer Commander Cousteau set sail on a round-the-world voyage on his *Alcyone*, equipped with two turbo-sail motors. Their driving force, with a surface area of 42 square metres, is equal to that of a 200 square metre conventional set of sails. As Cousteau wrote,

> Up to 20 knots the wind support is significant, but between 25 and 30 knots it becomes overwhelming and *Alcyone* made 20 knots through the water without any help from the diesel engines. Calculated over several half-day trials, we will have made fuel savings of between 50 and 60 per cent.[11]

In 1986 the US company Windstar Line Cruisers asked their shipyards in Le Havre to build them two cruise ships with 2,000 square metres of sail set on four 50-metre masts, which could be controlled by one man and a central computer processing weather information. The ships will cruise

---

[9] Laurent Schwarz, 'Vélo: l'innovation pousse à la roue', *Sciences et Avenir*, July 1991, p. 74.

[10] Ibid., p. 77.

[11] Commander Cousteau, 'On board l'*Alcyone* I celebrated the marriage of the wind and the water', *Paris Match*.

at 14 knots under wind-power and 12 knots with their diesel electric motors.

Back to the canals

Ships are here to stay. No less than two-thirds of international trade is transported in cargo ships on the sea-lanes and inland waterways of the world. Cargo planes have made virtually no impact on the transport of goods; the cost of water transport is approximately one-sixth that of road haulage, two-thirds that of rail transport, and a tiny proportion of air freight. It has been calculated that one horse power could transport 150 kilogrammes by road, 500 kg by train, and 4,000 kg by inland waterways.

In this domain as in other traditional systems, techniques have been modernised. Containers are increasingly being used, mounted on hydraulic or electric-powered lifts; inclined planes equipped with very powerful machinery make it possible to shift barges out of the water and on to trucks. A US technique which is increasingly used throughout the world is for barges to be pushed instead of towed along canals. There are many advantages in pushing lines of barges, including economies of men and engines, maximal use of payload volume, space-saving and the possibility of using a single propulsion unit for two strings of barges.

After the Second World War the growth of transport on inland waterways in Europe was dramatic, except in the UK where the network of eighteenth-century canals could not be modernised. A number of international authorities coordinated the changes on the continent, resulting in an enlarged and standardised system capable of taking craft up to 1,350 tonnes. Most of Europe's rivers were made navigable and new canals were dug to link east with west, north with south.

Within the European Community 38 per cent of goods are transported by water, representing some 200 million tonnes. On average, a 95-metre barge can take 90 trucks or 60 freight wagons of goods.

Perhaps the most spectacular waterway project, however, was the opening in 1959 of the St Lawrence Seaway, a joint Canadian/US project. Linking the Atlantic Ocean to the Great Lakes in the heart of the USA over a distance of some 4,000 kilometres, the canal is navigable by ocean-going ships.

Navigation and the commercial developments which it offers have sparked off an industrial and agricultural boom in the Great Lakes region. The renovation of apparently antiquated technologies can promote prosperity and enhance the future.

CHAPTER 5

Materials: Back to Basics

There was a Stone Age, a Bronze Age and an Iron Age – and then there was to be a Plastic Age: but somehow this never quite materialised. The glamour of nylon faded as artificial materials became synonymous with 'ersatz', a poor substitute rather than a genuine alternative.

Later still, when plastics came to be despised as environmentally hostile, manufacturers embarked on research programmes to create biodegradable forms.

The first plastic was created over a century ago, in the 1860s when John Wesley Hyatt made celluloid from nitrocellulose and camphor. The intention was to imitate natural materials such as ivory with something cheaper and more durable.

In 1907 Leo Baekeland invented Bakelite as a cheap substitute for lacquered or varnished wood.

Originally these materials were primarily admired for their durability. The first vinyl was used for gramophone records in the late 1920s, followed by cellophane, a new packaging material.

However, it was Du Pont's launch of nylon in the late 1930s which made the first headline sensations. Nylon stockings first went on view at New York's World Fair in 1939. Once they reached the stores, Du Pont could not manufacture them fast enough to keep up with demand. There were riots:

> Du Pont made a film, shown at the National Press Club, showing two women wrestling over a pair of nylons beneath the astonished gaze of the sales assistant. Another film clip shows the famous American comedian Bob Hope listening to screams backstage and commenting to the audience, 'They must have nylons back there!'

Nylon was declared a strategic material in the Second World War for parachutes and other items. It was unobtainable for civilian purposes until 1945, apart from a few pairs of stockings to be found on the black market; legend has it that a US soldier offering a pair of nylons could obtain anything he wanted from a woman in any war zone.

An article in a 1950 issue of L'Illustration stated that:

> The guide to plastic materials is becoming as big as a telephone directory. Have we joined the Plastic Age without knowing it?

Whatever happened to plastics?

Jeffrey L Meikle, an historian specialising in the impact of plastics on US culture, wrote of 'endless predictions of a world made better by plastics' but continued:

> The industry realised as early as 1943 that they would not live up to expectations. Meanwhile plastics produced for the home front were shoddy. Soon plastic manufacturers were back to imitating marble with vinyl and wood with formica and the plastic-for-plastic movement was dead.[1]

Revival and renewed condemnation came at the same time in the 1960s. Glamorised by the space programme, synthetics took on an air of enchantment, with fashions for foam houses and beanbag chairs made of vinyl. Andy Warhol was reported to have resolved the imitation/reality argument by saying 'It's not fake anything, it's real plastic'. Then came the popular film *The Graduate* in 1967, in which a middle-aged business-man mystifies young Dustin Hoffman by telling him: 'I just want to say one word to you. Just one word ... Plastics.' The word plastic became a synonym for 'fraudulent' or 'superficial' and seemed to represent a whole generation of parents with dreams not only of a US empire but of dominating the whole natural world.

What is perhaps the most extraordinary aspect of this U-turn in atti-tudes to plastics is probably the comment made during the fiftieth anniversary celebration of the invention of nylon, organised by Du Pont de Nemours. Julian W. Hill, one of Wallace D. Carothers' assistants in the creation of this revolutionary material, spoke out strongly in criti-cism of it:

> I think the human race is going to perish by being smothered in plas-tic. You have all these goddam plastic bags wrapping the garbage up where I have a summer house in Martha's Vineyard, and so nothing breaks down. It makes me wonder sometimes. I have always been a bird watcher and interested in nature. I get all these magazines and there's nothing in them but horror stories. Everywhere I look is a crumpled piece of plastic. My God, even in the fast-food places, you get a Styro-foam box this big.[2]

Has any inventor in history ever made such an unrestrained attack on one of his inventions?

---

[1] Quoted in 'Nylons, the Golden Age of Legs and the Progress of Plastic', *The International Herald Tribune*, 19 January 1988.

[2] Ibid.

There were certainly horror stories. In 1959 more than fifty children were suffocated by polyethylene dry cleaning bags. Du Pont declined all responsibility and blamed 'parental carelessness'. Environmentalists bemoaned seagulls crippled by plastic six-pack beer can matrices, and turtles strangling in plastic bags.

Mountains of synthetic polymer rubbish are piling up. Plastic cups, bottles and picnic cutlery litter beaches and roadsides all over the world, resisting degradation by water, rain, air or ultraviolet sunrays and microorganisms. Panic is taking over. In 1989 the USA had legislation pending on sixty-six proposed bans on non-biodegradable packaging, twelve packaging taxes, seventy-four recycling orders and nineteen requirements for states to purchase recycled materials.

These circumstances relating to plastics should not obscure the fact that these materials continue to be used in industry and in the home. It should simply be noted that the prophesies about the future of plastics have proved as unreal as those on the information technology revolution and the conquest of space.

Back to cotton

We are also turning back to natural materials such as cotton, wool, silk and linen: the general public has gradually discovered that 'It's not healthy' to wear nylon. Socks are now made of thread consisting of 25 per cent synthetics and 75 per cent cotton.

The fashion magazines show a distinct preference for entirely natural fabrics. The July 1989 issue of *Harper's and Queen* contained a Swiss advertisement which read:

> Those who loved Heidi must surely fall victim to the simple charm of this 100 per cent Swiss cotton shirt whose natural richness embodies at once the healthy, sweeping romance of the Alps and the sophistication of smart summer lunches.

The same issue offers 'a brilliant canary-coloured little suit ... in cotton denim which is the pinnacle of youth and vigour'. The magazine *Elle* showed a double-breasted, fully lined navy coat in 100 per cent cotton velvet. Marks & Spencer have men's shirts made of pure cotton and Bentalls in Kingston, Ealing, Worthing, Bracknell and Tonbridge offer heavy ribbed cotton velvet trousers.

Back to wool, silk, linen ...

The return to wool is more spectacular. As an advertisement claims, 'Wool talks your language', while every advertisement stresses that you are being offered only 100 per cent pure wool; merino wool is soft and sensual and machine-washable. There are even coats made of a camel-hair/cashmere blend.

This return to the past also includes silk, the very epitome of luxury, at highly competitive prices. A full-page advertisement in the *Sunday Times* supplement urges the merits of 'Special pure silk enchantment. Blouse available in two lovely shades of white and peach. Sizes 32"–40". Hand washable'. But silk is not reserved only for women – for men there are ties, underpants ...

Linen too is making a come back, as is leather: sheepskin jackets, suede waistcoats, leather gloves, riding boots, not to mention the 'finest soft Icelandic mountain lambskin'.

These advertising pages are of course generally to be found in 'quality' papers and magazines. They express a wish to return to nature, a characteristic of a sophisticated society in decline which prefers to ignore the materialism and ugliness of the industrial suburbs which were, and per-haps still are, the source of its wealth. This return to nature is reminiscent of French society in the late eighteenth century when the Queen of France, absorbed by her farm, remarked of the peasants who had no bread, 'Let them eat cake'.[3]

One area where plastics could have made important inroads is archi-tecture – yet this has not happened. Plasticised fabrics have been used as coverings in some cases, for example to protect semi-open stands as at Lord's cricket ground where reinforced fabric is stretched between metallic masts. The life of these materials is not expected to exceed ten or fifteen years. Nevertheless, we may well see this type of covering fabric – some of which is biodegradable – increasingly used in the building trade. Already fabrics originally made in single thickness are being lined to pro-vide for insulation layers.

Back to the Iron Age

It is remarkable that at the dawn of the third millennium we are still liv-ing in the Iron and Steel Age. The largest building sites in the world are those where metal-framed superstructures are going up. London, for example, has a fifty-storey tower being built at the rate of one floor per day. A crescent-shaped steel block of offices has risen over Charing Cross station on the Embankment. In recent years the building industry's pas-sion for reinforced concrete façades has faded. Its use has become wide-spread since the late 1840s when the French gardener, Joseph Monier, made concrete tubs reinforced with steel rods for his orange trees; it is relatively cheap and easy to use, and builders were convinced that it

---

[3] Jean-Jacques Rousseau, *Confessions*, VI.

would outlast all challenges – yet today it is clear that many reinforced concrete structures are rusting and cracking.

It is estimated that some three billion tonnes of concrete are used each year, or three-quarters of a tonne per person. No other material except water is used in such quantities.

What causes the cracks? They are the result of salts containing chloride ions which destroy the protective effects of the steel rods' cement shield. Carbon dioxide and industrial pollutants from the air also help to destroy the protective shield. In the Middle East the use of brackish water and sand containing chloride salts continues; the Armenian earthquake in 1988 revealed this weakness – but it also happens in the UK where the workforce, often poorly trained, applies a layer of cement which is too thin to protect buildings from the air.

Builders and road engineers are shocked and dismayed. In Montreal, for example, kilometres of concrete highways and bridges are being rebuilt at an exorbitant cost to the federal and local authorities. Roads are eaten away by the salt which is used to keep them free from frost and snow. Yet, according to a report published in April 1989,[4] the situation is not much better in the UK, where bridges are deteriorating much faster than anticipated by the Department of Transport. This survey indicates that one-fifth of the nine thousand road bridges in the country are in such poor condition that the affected parts must be completely cut away and rebuilt.

There is a substitute for salt, urea, which could be used; but engineers see little future for it, because urea costs ten times more than salt and is less effective in really bad weather conditions. Moreover, engineers claim that there is also a risk if urea filters through into water reserves and causes ammonia contamination. Urea has been used at only two sites in the UK by the Ministry of Transport, the Severn Bridge and 'Spaghetti Junction', both of which have suffered severe corrosion. According to the same report, little can be done to stop the progress of such corrosion.

Back to blood concrete

To forestall stains and cracks the French firm Innobat has developed a new type of concrete, based on dried animal blood, which makes it both stronger and lighter and improves its resistance to water. This is not a new technique – the Romans used blood (said by some to have included human blood) to strengthen their mortar.

To thwart negative criticisms of concrete the International Concrete Brick Association has launched a publicity campaign to promote the sale of concrete bricks which look more and more like traditional bricks. One

---

[4] *The Performance of Concrete Bridges - A Survey of 200 Highway Bridges*, (HMSO, 1989).

of their advertisements contrasted a drab-looking caterpillar with the emergence of a beautifully coloured butterfly. The caption read:

> There was a time when the appeal of concrete bricks lay solely in their durability, their strength and their competitive prices. Today they are now available in practically any colour you can think of. Not to mention a vast array of appealing textures.

The world of concrete is fighting back, but with what chances of success?

Back to brick

The fact that the manufacturers of concrete bricks are doing their best to copy the traditional clay brick which is some 5,000 years old is a telling reflection of the growing impact of bricks on the building trade in recent decades, particularly in the UK. Since concrete has not achieved the predicted results, brick has recently enjoyed a fresh surge of interest. This is due in part to its traditional look which is so highly prized today. Even modernist architects such as Piano are using bricks for cladding.

The techniques used by the brick industry have been much improved, with advances in calculations and design offering better use of the material. In particular, reinforced brickwork has been greatly improved by the Ceramic Research Association. But reinforced brickwork is not new. It was used to strengthen construction throughout the nineteenth century, one notable example being Sir Marc Brunel's use of it in the construction of the Thames tunnel in 1820. During the first thirty years of the twentieth century, Alexander Brebner used it in India and later the concept was revived for the development of earthquake-resistant structures, particularly in the USA. The UK has now built a reinforced brick bridge.

In addition to its use as a structural material, brick is increasingly used for cladding on high-rise concrete buildings, to protect them from airborne industrial pollutants.

Back to timber-framed houses

In recent years the sale of timber-framed houses has grown dramatically in the UK – they can even be bought in kit form. Timber construction offers better insulation, and the owner of a timber-framed house can enjoy seeing his heating bills substantially reduced. This may explain why 90 per cent of houses in North America and Scandinavia (hardly noted for their low standard of living) are built in this way.[5]

Timber frames can often be built faster than masonry frames, for only dry materials are involved; further, wood is lighter and therefore easier

---

[5] José Manser, *Building Homes Supplement*, 11 August 1989, p. 30.

to transport to the site.

Early Breton and Norman settlers in North America in the sixteenth and seventeenth centuries probably took their own stonemasons with them to build new stone houses exactly like their traditional homes in Europe. But they soon discovered that in these northern latitudes their new homes were bitterly cold to live in. They realised that stone offers poor heat insulation, and followed the example of other European colonists who lived in log cabins offering much better protection against the icy Arctic winds.

Back to earth-built houses

Earth walls provide excellent insulation against tropical winds. I visited Timbuktu to see three enormous Archimedean Screws, each one 12 metres long and weighing 6 tonnes, built by the *Iles de Paix*, the very successful Belgian organisation founded by the Nobel Peace Prize winner Father Pire to irrigate the Sahara desert. Inside the earth built house which had belonged to Ahmed Baba – one of the great Islamic intellectuals of the sixteenth century – I observed men in the courtyard building an air-conditioned stone room for UNESCO, to preserve the scholar's precious manuscripts. The stone, which looked remarkably like the stone of Chartres cathedral, came from a quarry less than 10 kilometres away. I promptly enquired why, if such high-quality stone was available so near, it had not been used for building Timbuktu itself. The reply was equally prompt: stone lacks insulating qualities and will not keep out the heat as effectively as earth. Having been brought up to admire Europe's stone cathedrals, I was ignorant of the extraordinary properties of wood and earth.

To protect himself against Californian heat, ex-President Reagan, the promoter of Star Wars, has come down to earth and has had his latest ranch built of earth, following old Indian and Spanish techniques which have been revived since the 1973 oil crisis. In the USA the practice of building earth houses never really disappeared; 160,000 such houses were still being built each year circa 1970, particularly in the states of the south-west and most notably in New Mexico.

The most famous US architect, Frank Lloyd Wright, drew plans in 1942 for a luxurious earth villa, the Pottery House. It was eventually built in 1985 and sold for no less than $2.2m. Earth has its price! Towards the end of the 1970s other opulent mud villas were built for various multimillionaires by the architect William Lumpkins; there was the Balcombe Residence at Santa Fe, which combined mud bricks and solar energy panels, and a sumptuous villa near Taos, both in New Mexico.

Certain residential zones in New Mexico show the same modern influence, such as La Luz in the suburbs of Albuquerque, where dried brick has been used for public buildings.

What is surprising in all these south-western states of the US, and also in Latin America, is the durability of the material. Sun-dried buildings in two distinct traditions, Indian and Spanish, survive well, often undamaged.

The Peruvian city of Chan Chan, built by the Chimu civilisation in the thirteenth century, is considered the world's largest town built of dried earth. The tradition continued after the Spanish Conquest and Lima, the capital of Peru, can still boast the largest cathedral ever built of earth.

Across the Pacific, long sections of the Great Wall of China were built of dried earth. Today this is the material chosen by China to build the largest dam in the world with a potential of 13,000 megawatts – 15 per cent of China's electricity.

Many of the great legendary cities of the world were built of mud. It is said that the Tower of Babel, the world's first skyscraper which was believed to have reached 90 metres in height, was also made of earth. In the Near East the technique was still in use in recent times; Tabriz and Seojane in Iran and Saada in Yemen are there to be admired – but the greatest of such cities is undoubtedly Shibam in the Yemen where the old town still has some five hundred buildings, the majority between seven and ten storeys high.

Back to unbaked brick

One of the twentieth-century pioneers of the present-day trend back to earth construction was the Egyptian architect Hassan Fathy. He was principally interested in 'architecture for the poor', the title of his world-famous book.[6]

Hassan Fathy's aim was essentially to supply the rural poor with houses built of unbaked brick, which they could afford. He was fighting an influential lobby to build in modern materials, particularly cement, which have to be imported by developing countries and paid for out of their meagre foreign resources. Cement is capital intensive while mud brick construction is more labour intensive and cheaper to use.

Although his influence was considerable outside his own country – he was even invited to build a mosque with mud bricks in Abiquiu in New Mexico, where the bricks are known as *adobe* – in Egypt it was limited, as his efforts to build rural villages came up against local socio-economic problems. Hassan Fathy devoted half his life to creating homes for prosperous Egyptians, even though that was not precisely what he had hoped to do.

---

[6] Hassan Fathy, *Architecture for the Poor*, (Chicago 1973).

An eighteenth-century return to earth

One hundred and fifty years ago the French architect François Contereaux, born in Lyon in 1740, sought to improve earth buildings for the poor and for the burgeoning middle classes, with the same social fervour as Hassan Fathy. He was to promote the improvement not of mud bricks but of another material, rammed earth or *pisé*. This consists of soil mixed with straw and gravel and compressed. Writing at the time of the Enlightenment and the French Revolution, he asserted that, 'the precious art of *pisé* is for an enlightened nation a sure way to achieve the blossoming of its rural regions, its trade and its industry'.[7]

Like those of Hassan Fathy, Contereaux's books were to be widely read and absorbed abroad. The cover of the English edition in 1806 read: 'A Treatise on Pisé Building as recommended by the Board of Agriculture with improvements by the author.' This edition reached Australia and the USA and architects as well-known as Henry Holland and Clough Williams-Ellis were to be influenced by his work.

But unlike Fathy, Contereaux's influence in his own country was great and lasting. Many great bourgeois homes built in *pisé* have survived, as well as schools and factories. One remarkable architectural ensemble still standing is Saint Siméon de Bressieux, about 50 kilometres north-west of Grenoble. This is a *cité ouvrière*, a working class housing complex three storeys high and covering 4,400 square metres.

The fashion for *pisé* building lasted in France until the First World War. By the early 1920s enthusiasm had faded, for various economic, industrial, social, psychological and cultural reasons; yet this renaissance of *pisé*, which lasted for more than a century, indicates that the return to the technology of the past, intelligently modernised – the theme of this book – can have a very successful future.

A twentieth-century return to earth

It is no coincidence that today's revival of dried earth buildings should be centred near Lyon, the birthplace of François Contereaux and the ancient Roman capital of the Gauls; their houses were mainly built of mud bricks and *pisé*. A pilot settlement of mud-brick buildings for low rental, *Le Domaine de la Terre* in the new city of L'Isle d'Abeau[8] was constructed in the same way. It was built to prove to the West that there was a future in earth buildings: and to prove to the Third World that developed countries could also make use of humble forms of technology. But

---

[7] Quoted in Jean Dethier, *Architecture de Terre*, (Paris, 1986), p. 17.

[8] *Le Domaine de la Terre* can be reached by the A43 motorway (Lyon-Geneva) or by the A43 (Lyon-Grenoble). Exit, *L'Isle d'Abeau Est*.

often resentment arises when the west attempts to impose superseded technologies on them; they feel that we recommend what is of no further use to us.

Needless to say, the manufacture of earth bricks and *pisé* has been improved through the use of advanced twentieth-century technology. The earth is subjected to laboratory analysis and, depending on its constitution, bitumen or cement may be added to improve its water resistance and to obtain a stabilised product.[9]

The Western World/Third World dialogue

By drawing attention to his book *Architecture for the Poor* Hassan Fathy has reawakened western interest in a long-neglected material. This was one of those rare instances when the West acknowledged that it had something to learn from the ancient common heritage of mankind. Perhaps further feedback of this kind from the Third World may reduce the hazards looming for the high-tech world: yet it is unlikely that such feedback will bring more than marginal benefits.

All the same, a dialogue of this kind may be accompanied by suspicion of western motives, and third world nations have a tendency to brush aside advice on the use of low cost technology. Projects such as the *Domaine de la Terre* are probably far more persuasive than words alone; for developing countries, concrete symbolises everything that is modern and desirable. Yet such a tendency can be reversed, as can be seen in industrial countries; there must be awareness of the limitations of concrete. This was noted by the Algerian architect Noui-Mehedi describing the experience of a peasant who was given a badly built concrete house by his local municipal authorities. 'Only a few months sufficed for the humidity to cause the whole family to flee from their home. Today that family is living in a house with a thatched roof and is keeping its cattle in the concrete house ...'[10]

Back to the Stone Age

Although the insulation properties of stone are less favourable than those of many other building materials,

> several factors are contributing to the rise of a Stone age, the most prominent being energy saving, environmental considerations and technological developments ... stone quarrying is the largest extractive industry by volume with coal and petroleum trailing behind and iron

---

[9] 'Small Scale manufacture of stabilised soil blocks', *Technological Memorandum no. 12*, ILO Technology Series, (Geneva, 1987).

[10] Anil Agarwal, *Mud, Mud*, (London, 1981), p. 29.

ore, salt and sulphur very much lower on the scale.[11]

The volume of stone handled is increasing substantially every year. It is estimated that the world now uses 25–30 million tonnes annually, over 60 per cent being granite, a strong durable stone – much more so than marble – and which can survive in very polluted environments. This explains why it is so much in demand all over the world, and why it is used for facing and cladding concrete buildings. South Africa is the world's largest granite exporter.

These are the modern tools which make granite a growth industry. Indeed, thanks to modern techniques we can now rapidly extract and dress enormous quantities, whereas formerly it was beyond man's powers to use this stone which was too hard for his primitive tools.

Into the Ceramic Age?

Ceramic is the first artificial material, dating back to the seventh century BC. It is now coming to the fore once again with the introduction of advanced technology in its manufacture and the identification of new outlets.

To enable the space shuttle to return to earth the engineers needed a material capable of resisting the very high re-entry temperatures. The only suitable material was ceramic, and thus it came about that the heat shield, consisting of 33,000 ceramic tiles, was applied to the body of the shuttles.

Scientists have established that a particular type of ceramic has super-conducting properties, at temperatures much higher than those of other known super-conductors. Ceramics are used to make knife blades which never wear out, and for roof tiles.

One country which is profiting from the expanding ceramic tile industry is Italy:

the output has escalated from nearly 38 million square metres of tile in 1960 to over 355 million in 1980. In the same period the proportion of export went from 3.5 per cent in 1960 to 45 per cent in 1980, giving Italy a clear lead in the world market.[12]

The industry is chiefly based in the provinces of Modena and Reggio Emilia.

In fact Italy has been the most successful country in introducing high-tech into traditional technologies and should be identified as the model

---

[11] Asher Shadmon, *Stone*, (London, 1989), p. 4.

[12] Margharita Russo, *Technical Change and the Industrial District. The role of inter-firm relations in the growth and transformation of ceramic tile production in Italy*, ed. Edward

for countries which seek to improve their overall economic performance. Edward Goodman is founder of the Acton Society and editor of the book *Small Firms and Industrial Districts in Italy*,[13] in which he describes how this success was accomplished. The Italian achievement is based on the *Artigiano* firms rooted in the family and grounded in the community where values, beliefs, loyalties and interests are held in common. In 1985 the *Artigiano* firm employing fewer than ten workmen represented up to 80 per cent of all manufacturing firms in central and north-eastern Italy, substantially out-performing large businesses in the same industrial sector; moreover, their wages were at that time significantly higher.

Certain cities such as Modena have created 'craftsmen' villages, where production sites and residential zones are no more than walking or cycling distance apart, where information centres for the unemployed feed directly into newly established companies and where small companies using computerised techniques operate together to manufacture complex products.

> ...It is very impressive to see how many people live in Italy in a world similar to the pre-industrial age while this nation is considered a credible model of the post-industrial world.[14]

And when our civilisation finally collapses – our banking and financial system is already hanging by a thread – when the multinationals disintegrate, the *Artigiano* businesses which are so much more flexible will adapt to the new economic circumstances. It will not be the first time that Italy will have survived and prospered after a financial catastrophe.

In the fourteenth century, as today, developing nations had debts and banks feared that the Third World nations of the day would not be able to repay them. the UK was one such country at that time, and when in 1337 she was unable to meet her debts, she caused the collapse of the Bardi and Peruzzi banks in Florence, the Wall Street of the day. Small Florentine banks collapsed like houses of cards. The memory of this financial disaster has never completely faded in Italy and since then the Peruzzi family has been seeking compensation from the British government. It was indeed reported that if Italy had been victorious in the Second World War, Mussolini would have included in the Peace Treaty a clause whereby the UK would repay the capital and 600 years of interest. The grand total was estimated in the 1930s to be roughly the equivalent of the value of the British Empire.

---

[13] Edward Goodwood, *Small Firms and Industrial Districts in Italy*, Routledge, (London 1889), p. 4.

[14] Colin Ward, 'Can they make jobs too? The Italian lesson', *Welcome in Inner City*, (London, 1989), p. 91.

CHAPTER 6

Live Longer – Suffer More

In their book *The Year 2000*, published in 1967, Hermann Kahn and Anthony Wiener predicted the eradication of disease by the beginning of the twenty-first century:[1] but bubonic plague is still with us. A late nineteenth-century outbreak of this terrible scourge of mankind spread from China to the west coast of the USA in 1900, resulting in thirteen deaths in Oakland in 1919 and thirty-four in Los Angeles in 1924. What worries the US medical authorities is the real risk of an epidemic, because it is now not only rats which bear the plague bacillus: it is carried by a whole range of rodents, including the squirrels which have distributed the plague across much of the south-western USA. A medievalist known to the author, Sarah Ferguson, caught the plague on a visit to New Mexico; as a student of the Middle Ages she immediately recognised the symptoms and was astonished that her friends were not surprised by the illness. She was treated and cured with penicillin.

Although antibiotics can cure plague, they are ineffective against AIDS, which is constantly referred to in the press as the plague of our own time, a present-day form of the Black Death. Today's fear of the virus would seem to create a mentality similar to that of medieval times.

AIDS has forced public opinion to recognise that medicine is not heading ever onward and upward. Mass production of a vaccine will take many years, despite all efforts to produce and market such a product. Even when a vaccine is available at some future date, many countries in Africa, Asia and South America will never possess the financial and administrative resources to restrict the spread of the virus. As with the plague in medieval Europe, perhaps one-third of the population may succumb to the disease.

---

[1] Herman Kahn and Anthony Wiener, *The Year 2000 - a Framework for Speculation on the Next Thirty-Three Years*, (London, 1968).

Tropical diseases – a persistent stumbling block

It is often not realised that we still have no vaccines against five of the major tropical diseases – bilharzia (schistomatosis), trypanosomiasis (sleeping sickness), filariasis, leishmaniasis and leprosy. Of these, three can be treated reasonably effectively – bilharzia, filariasis and leprosy – but no effective drugs have yet been discovered for treating the remaining two.

The tragedy is that in the Third World, the home of three-quarters of the world's population and birthplace of 86 per cent of it, tropical diseases are in general not fading away but spreading. This is a striking confirmation that progress is on the wane. It is a blow to our cherished idea of continuing advance, of making the world a better place for all to live in, a blow to scientists and to our much-vaunted liberal society. The most lamentable aspect is the pharmaceutical industry's failure to persist in developing new vaccines: 'Vaccines account for only 1 per cent of the pharmaceutical industry's profits.'[2]

The fault is not solely the responsibility of western culture, for the Third World spends very little on health. The statistics for the world's 40 poorest countries in 1988 show expenditure of 13.8 per cent of national income on defence, against a modest 5.5 per cent on health.

The losing battle against the spread of tropical diseases has finally persuaded scientists to tone down their optimism and recognise the failure of their 1960s predictions. André Capron, director of immunology and parasite biology at the Institut Pasteur in Lille, acknowledges this truth: 'We offered false hopes.'[3] Parasites and the human immune system are much more complex than had ever been imagined.

One of the greatest worries in the medical world in recent years is the dramatic spread of malaria. The number of people suffering and dying from this terrible disease is staggering. WHO (the World Health Organisation) estimates that 200–300 million are infected each year and 2–3 million die world-wide. Some 1,700 million carry the disease.

Since the 1960s one of the most deadly malaria parasites, *plasmodium falciparium*, has become resistant to the 'wonder-drug', choroquine (nivaquine). It is now feared that this parasite may eventually become resistant to the new drugs mefloquine and halofantine. Meanwhile, new outbreaks have swept through the Amazonian forests. In the 1950s Brazil had brought malaria under control, but the opening up of Amazonia to settlers and the subsequent gold rush meant that by 1988 there were half

---

[2] Corinna Jamma 'L'Offensive des maladies tropicales', *Sciences et Avenir*, October 1989, p. 93.

[3] Ibid.

a million cases of the disease in this newly-developed region now known as 'the malaria frontier'. While the advanced industrial countries of the world have done little to develop a vaccine against malaria, a Third World country, Columbia, has succeeded. A Colombian doctor, Manuel Patarroyo, at the Immunological Institute in Bogotá has devised a vaccine which has gained acceptance among western scientists after years of scepticism.

Parasites have been with us since the dawn of time, with their burden of suffering and death. One of malaria's most famous victims was Alexander the Great, who caught the disease as he crossed the Tigris marshlands in Mesopotamia. Archaeology shows that bilharzia was rampant in Ancient Egypt and in China, where it still thrives, as in seventy-four other countries throughout the world. No less than 200 million people suffer its debilitating effects, with a further 500–600 million at risk.

One of the most dread diseases, tuberculosis (TB) remains a constant threat in the Third World. India is discovering that TB is its greatest single cause of death. In the western world it had practically disappeared with BCG inoculation, but is now tragically reappearing – especially in the USA where a new lethal TB strain is resistant to present-day drugs.

Control of the disease by tablets is proving problematic. The treatment involves taking a large number of pills each day for many months, but sufferers usually feel fit after only a few weeks. In New York city, where the disease is epidemic, the authorities are interning tubercular patients if they fail to take their tablets.

For fifteen years I have been using a three-dimensional model to teach people in Third World countries like Kenya, India and Nepal that they should continue taking their tablets regularly. Thousands of lives have thus been saved. The model has an incomparable advantage over lectures, film, television and other audio-visual techniques in that it is tactile, thereby transcending all language barriers. Following an article published by Phyllida Brown[4], which suggested that this type of model could be of great assistance in the west, the London Chest Hospital has ordered two models for their own use from the artist, Katya Follett.

This is yet another example of a traditional method which is more efficient and less costly than sophisticated audio-visual techniques.

The thriving western diseases

Is it not surprising that, although some diseases have effectively vanished from the western world, the common cold is still very much with us? Another of the prophesies of the 1950s and 1960s was that it would soon be a thing of the past. In 1959 Thomas Ward, a virus research scien-

---

[4] *New Scientist*, 4 September 1993.

tist at the University of Notre Dame in the USA, developed a vaccine against eight viruses which would, he said, wipe out the majority of cold infections. Now retired, Dr Ward admits more humbly: 'Every time we identified a virus causing upper respiratory infections, others would appear.' He acknowledged that 'even if it were possible to develop a vaccine against the several hundred constantly mutating rhinoviruses, the reactions would be worse than the common cold itself'.[5] Nature is decidedly not a friendly area to work in.

A more serious illness which has been with us since early classical times is influenza (flu). It was described by the great French doctor Ambroise Paré in 1510:

> They had great pain in the head, all over the stomach, kidneys and legs and had continuous fever with delirium and frenzy.

Paré's description could well apply to the 1988 flu epidemic which in France alone attacked 4,360,000 victims. Some died, although not as many as in the pandemic of 1729–30 when the virus swept through Europe and the New World, causing, it was said at the time, more deaths than the Great Plague of London in 1665. But this pestilence was nothing compared to the Spanish Flu epidemic at the end of the First World War which caused some 20,000,000 deaths – more than the number killed in battle during the war itself. Fifty per cent of the world's population are thought to have suffered from the virus between April 1918 and May 1919; only a few islands, like New Guinea and St Helena escaped. The pandemic of 1988 proved that we have no protection against any new 'Spanish 'flu'.

The West also continues to suffer from cancer, a disease which dates back to time immemorial. The oldest known case is that of a nine year old child who lived 120 thousand years ago and whose fossilised body was found in a cave in southern France. The child had died of a brain cancer. The illness was described in an Egyptian papyrus dating from the fifteenth century BC, and the great Greek doctor Hippocrates was much concerned by it. Ambroise Paré, quoted above, believed that cancer was the result of an unhealthy way of life and was the first to suggest operating on tumours. The first hospital to treat cancer was in Rheims where, in 1740, experiments were carried out on treatment for breast cancer.

In developed countries, one person in six is destined to die of cancer. It will kill some 500,000 Americans this year, while another million will discover during the year that they are sufferers. The number of deaths from cancer in the USA is growing rather than declining, up by 8 per cent per

---

[5] Randolph P. Smith, 'False Prophesies – From cancer to the common cold predicting a cure has been easier than coming up with one', *Wall Street Journal*, 13 November 1989.

year since the early 1950s. What a blow to the pretensions of the scientists who were so confident of solving this major human problem! They have not lacked funds.

Over the past several decades no other disease has proved so resistant to forecasts of defeat. With each discovery researchers predicted that a treatment effective against one form of cancer might solve the whole mystery. Such claims were made for the anti-viral vaccine L-Asparaginase, Interferon, and more recently immunotherapy and gene therapy. In the late 1960s George E. Moore, former director of the Rosewall Park Cancer Institute at Buffalo, NY, predicted the development of a vaccine against many cancers – but the prophesy has yet to come true.

A drug industry prone to heart failure

The number of deaths from heart disease is even greater, and here too the predictions of the 1960s have failed to materialise. In 1967 Irvine Page, a leading heart researcher at the Cleveland Clinic Foundation in the USA, asserted that heart disease would have virtually disappeared by the year 2000: yet in 1990 cardiovascular disease lay behind 44 per cent of deaths in the USA while 171,577 deaths from heart disease were recorded in France.

Although the drug industry has turned away from tropical disease it has invested heavily in more specifically western diseases in recent years, although still with little result. The limited number of new drugs and poor profitability have restrained Wall Street and the City from investment in the once promising biotechnological area of the industry. Industrial experts say that investors who once seemed to have bottomless pockets have stopped putting in money at precisely the critical moment when the biotechnology companies are in greatest need of capital to pursue their researches. The experts blame the Wall Street crash of October 1987, when many biotechnology stocks plunged; in addition the failure of a new and widely-publicised drug restricted the flow of fresh investment capital.

This new drug was Tissue Plasminogen Activator (TPA), which was sold under the name of Activase and was the first major product of the biotechnology industry. Created by Genentech in the USA, it was designed to dissolve blood clots blocking the coronary arteries. The mass media were summoned on 29 May 1987 to witness the launch of this revolutionary medication; but in the late afternoon, contrary to all Genentech plans, the advisory committee of the Food and Drugs Administration (FDA), refused to allow sales of Activase. Further trials were required. The launch collapsed in total confusion, with Hollywood-style scenes of financial journalists rushing for the door and pulling out their portable phones as they ran. Genentech's shares dropped by several billion dollars and shares in other companies in the drugs sector also fell.

The man in the street is right to be surprised at seeing potentially health-giving drugs subject to the whims of the Stock Market. After fresh trials the FDA relented. Investors discovered that sales of Activase were lower than expected and turned away from Genentech, thus restricting dramatically the firm's research potential, to the detriment of the sick. Press announcements of a substantial investment in the company in 1990 by one of the largest Swiss pharmaceutical firms, Roche Holding Ltd., came as no surprise.

Excessive optimism over this drug was generated as much by enthusiastic cardiologists as by Genentech's own marketing. It was soon discovered that the cost of a single shot of TPA was $2,000, prohibitive for most hospitals except those treating the very wealthy.

The pharmaceuticals industry was confronted by the same problems as other industries where advanced technologies turn out to be much too costly. Furthermore, doctors soon became aware that Streptokinase, an anti-coagulant from the pre-genetic era, was almost as effective as TPA and one-tenth of the price, at $200 a dose. The result of the ISIS-3 trial published in April 1992 surprisingly suggested that Streptokinase was safe. Genentech's Safa was relaunched in 1993 when an international study found that TPA was marginally more efficient than Streptokinase. Within hours of the results being announced, the value of Genentech's shares leapt $4.75 on the New York Stock Exchange.

The FDA, a bureaucratic deathtrap

In defence of Genentech and the pharmaceutical firms which market costly drugs, it must be recognised that it is increasingly difficult to launch new products; manufacturers must reckon on nearly ten years of investment in research and then another two years of trials before obtaining FDA approval. It is therefore hardly surprising that the drug companies concentrate their efforts on a limited range of projects.

It is in the pharmaceutical industry that the disappearance of innovation is particularly dramatic. The number of drugs put on the market has declined enormously in recent years. As David Moreau, managing director of one of the UK's most innovative pharmaceutical companies, writes:

> Pharmaceutical research after its enormous peak in the fifties and sixties has slowed down considerably to a rate at which I wonder sometimes if some diseases will ever be conquered ... so that many of my generation will die of conditions that it is not economic to find an answer to.[5]

Regulations covering pharmaceutical products are far too strict. As an OECD publication states: 'The automatic adoption of new regulations has reduced or even destroyed innovation: if drugs like aspirin and penicillin were invented nowadays, they would never have passed current standards.'[6]

The fact that neither aspirin nor penicillin would meet today's standards shows clearly the decline in innovation in this late twentieth-century era. Every day millions of men and women would suffer from headaches if these regulations had been introduced earlier in the century, while millions more would have suffered and died without antibiotics.

Some twenty years ago, in his Institute for Arteriosclerosis in Los Angeles, the research scientist and humanist Professor Lester Morrisson developed a product which prevented arteriosclerosis – hardening of the arteries. However, the FDA insisted on tests which would have cost $35m before the sale could be authorised. Professor Morrisson had only $7m available, and was therefore forced to give up his plans to sell his miracle product in US pharmacies. And yet, with a slight modification of the formula – the removal of elastomucoprotease – the sale of Atherol has been permitted in US health stores since 1982. Certain differences in regulations between the UK and the USA have allowed the sale of Atherol by British high street chemists under the name of Arterol, with the full number of ingredients.

Arterol is one of the very few world drugs to slow the ageing process, but the FDA has persisted in ignoring it.

Human guinea-pigs

In 1982, while Arterol received no publicity, the Jarvis-7 artificial heart implanted into Barney Clark received the attention of the world's mass media for weeks on end. Was this because Arterol was too cheap a drug, costing about £90 per person per year, or because the Jarvis epic was sustained by powerful financial interests? In *Worse than the Disease – Pitfalls of Medical Progress* we can read 'the story of the uneasy marriage of commercialism with established scientific methods and government safeguards for the introduction of new and unproven technologies'.[7] The book reads like a Frankenstein tale.

As with the common cold, flu and cancer, there were predictions that hundreds of thousands of men and women would live for decades with artificial hearts. Here too these wild forecasts date back to the 1950s and 1960s. One of the pioneers of heart surgery, Michael Debakey, declared

---

[6] David Moreau, 'Malady without a cure', *The Chemical Engineer*, (1988), 33.

[7] OECD, *Technical Change and Economic Policy*, op. cit., p. 60.

that a permanent artificial heart would be perfected in the 1980s. Later, however, he recognised that 'we just did not have enough information to realise how complex the problem really is. We thought the heart was simply a mechanical pump to move blood'.[8] In 1982, in the very week of Barney Clark's operation, Dr Wilhelm Kolff, a pioneer of artificial heart implants, stated,

> Artificial heart recipients would be barred from marathons within fifteen years because they would be too strong.[9]

While Dr Kolff was making his wild assertions, Clark was beginning his life as a guinea pig. The facts recorded here were not publicised at the time but were concealed from the mass media. Forty-eight hours after the historic operation there was a tear in his lungs and air leaked into the tissue beneath the skin, requiring a half-hour operation to repair the leak. On the sixth post-operative day he suffered a series of seizures which lasted for two hours. After a fortnight the implanted heart began to fail. Clark had to undergo further open-heart surgery for the replacement of a broken valve in the artificial heart. In the sixth week he suffered severe nose-bleeds which required surgery to cauterise the bleeding artery. Later he developed pneumonia, kidney disease, gout and an intestinal ulcer. Finally he succumbed to generalised infection and lung failure; after 112 days his heart was finally at rest.

Antivivisectionists would do well to take an interest in the protection of human beings undergoing scientific experiments, and in marketing. Unfortunately Barney Clark was not to be the last guinea-pig. The longest-lived was William J. Schroeder, from Indiana. He survived for 21 months after a heart implant in 1984 followed by (only) two strokes, internal bleeding, fevers, depression, anaemia and a liver infection.

What is alarming is that it was not until the first week of February 1990 that the FDA withdrew its approval of the continued experiments with the Jarvis artificial heart. Faults had been found in the manufacturing process, and yet it had been known since 1982 that the valve which failed in Barney Clark's heart had failed several times during animal testing. It was known that the medical team who operated on Clark had not tested the machine for as long as was required for an operation on a human. Thus the FDA had allowed the torture of humans for several years when they could have saved the lives of millions by authorising the sale of Arterol in the USA on prescription in pharmacies. The FDA should perhaps be put on trial for crimes against humanity.

So the high-tech heart is now in limbo; but so too are many other high-tech artificial organs. The state of Utah created a Bionic Valley in Salt Lake

---

[8] Diana B. Dutton, *Worse than the Disease - Pitfalls of Medical Progress*, (Cambridge, 1988).

[9] *False Prophesies*, op. cit.

City, along the lines of California's computer-orientated Silicon Valley; today many of the firms in Bionic Valley have gone bankrupt, like so many in Silicon Valley. High-tech artificial arms were created there for the disabled, but at $40,000 each they were too costly. The same applied to artificial hands, and artificial ears have not met with much success.

Suffer more ...

That medical high-tech often fails may be a blessing in disguise. Prevention should take priority over curing. Because our life expectancy has lengthened considerably in the western world the number of years of suffering before death has increased significantly and dramatically. This fact of present-day living is rarely discussed openly, but a book by James Riley has finally opened the debate. It develops the thesis by which the longer we live the more we suffer from injury and disease. Factors which lead to a population's increased average age also add significantly to the risk of illness. 'The task humankind has set itself,' argues Riley, 'was not to preserve health but to extend the lifespan'.[10]

Such facts should perhaps lead us to ponder on mythological tales. Once upon a time there was a court physician – the eponymous Makropoulos of Janacek's opera – who discovered the elixir of life. His daughter drank it and regretted it for 600 years. The mixture which extended her life made her coldhearted and miserable. Finally she gave up drinking it and died content. Tithonous, another mythological character, was a worse case: when his lover asked Jupiter to make him immortal she forgot to ask for youthfulness as well and Tithonous was granted eternal senility. Another fictional case appears in Swift's *Gulliver's Travels*, in which the hero visits the country of the Luggnaggiens, home of the immortal *struldbrug* who:[11]

> at the age of 90 lose their teeth and their hair ... eat and drink without pleasure or appetite ... subject to continuous illness ... and at the end of 200 years they can no longer carry on conversation with their mortal neighbours; thus they are subject to the disagreeable condition of living as strangers in their own land.[12]

Swift commented that 'the reader may have no difficulty in believing that what I learned and saw had forcibly attenuated my desire for immortality'.[13]

---

[10] *Worse than the Disease*, op. cit., p. 120.

[11] James C Riley, *Sickness, Recovery and Death: A History of Forecast of Ill Health*, (London, 1989).

[12] Jonathan Swift, *Gullivers Travels*, first published 1726.

[13] Ibid.

Medicine has increased the expectancy of life far beyond its capacity to preserve its quality. The greater part of old age is spent in chronic illness and misery, with Alzheimer's Disease which erodes the brain, osteoarthritis, osteoporosis (thinning of the bones) which leads to fractures, deafness and incontinence. But also present in old age are the illnesses which have appeared earlier in life and which have never been completely cured – migraines which affect nearly 10 per cent of the population and for which there seems to be no real remedy, or arthritis.

A careful survey of the UK population has revealed 41 per cent of adults have taken pain killers, on average five times in the past two weeks; indeed in the past 24 hours. In the UK, 2,000 tons of aspirin are consumed annually. Try as they might, the pharmaceutical giants have not been able to produce effective drugs which avoid such side-effects as constipation (caused by morphine and codeine) and gastrointestinal haemorrhage (produced by high doses of aspirin and almost all of its synthetic cousins).

However, in 1974 scientists in the UK discovered that the central nervous system has the ability to produce its own pain-killing, morphine-like substances. If this system could be stimulated into action, patients would be able to produce their own, side-effect free, pain relief.

Without fully understanding the mechanisms, doctors have been using electricity to stimulate the nervous system to produce pain relief for a very long time. In the ancient world there was a variety of fish, including the torpedo ray (*Torpedo mamorata*) and the electric or Nile catfish (*Malopterus electricus*), whose existence was a source of both fear and superstitious conjecture because they could produce painful and paralysing shocks. Evidence discovered in Egyptian tombs built around 2750 BC, where they appear prominently, implies that they were probably used for medical purposes. The Romans rediscovered the phenomenon. In AD47, while walking on the beach, one of the Emperor Nero's freedmen accidentally obtained a cure from his gout by treading on a live torpedo ray. Where these fish were found, electricity of this kind was employed to relieve pain throughout the middle ages and up until the sixteenth century.

However, eighteenth and nineteenth century pioneers like Benjamin Franklin, Luigi Galvani, Alessandro Volta and Michael Faraday generated electricity from non-animal sources, so the nervous system could be stimulated safely in a controlled manner. Nowadays there is renewed interest in electrotherapeutic methods. Bristol doctors Alexander Macdonald and Tim Coates stimulate the spinal cord by means of electrodes placed on the skin. This method is painless and free from side effects, and can be carried out by patients at home. Because pain processing begins in the spinal cord, provided the nervous system itself is intact, this method is designed to bring relief to all parts of the body simultaneously. This twentieth century upgrade of a 5,000 year old technique could well be a record ...

Reappraisal of past medical practice

It is in many ways the failure of present-day medicine to preserve the quality of life that has led to the reappraisal of the witchdoctor and alternative therapies such as acupuncture, homeopathy, magnetism, naturopathy, somatherapy, magnetotherapy, osteopathy, yoga and others. It may also be due to the shortcomings of doctors as communicators. They frequently talk down to their patients, while 'healers' generally have a more caring and personal relationship with sufferers.

The trend towards the irrational, the mystical and to Eastern cults is a course often followed by societies that are ageing or in decline. It happened in Alexandria. Today, France has more astrologers than priests. It is estimated that one in every three people in modern society has consulted a healer at one time or another; often, it must be admitted, with success.

This drift back towards esoteric cults is also combined with a return to pre-Christian or Roman nature cults, with belief in nymphs and gods in streams, trees and mountains. Christianity brought a profound change in this attitude; as Lynn White wrote:

> For Christians, saints and angels genuinely existed. But the spirit inhabiting an object or a place, the spirit of the place which must not be upset or disturbed, had no further importance.[14]

This explains why Europe, psychologically liberated, was able to destroy nature with impunity and create industrial revolutions, first in medieval times and then in the eighteenth and nineteenth centuries. It also explains to a large extent what David Landes calls 'European exceptionalism'. The present day return to nature exemplified by the ecology movement is an instinctive reaction against the industrialisation of Europe during the last thousand years and thus against high tech.

So we are going back to Roman times and aquatherapy, to cures in spas like Bath and Vichy, seeking treatment for asthma, rheumatism or skin problems. We are returning to even older times, to the frankincense and myrrh which the Three Wise Men brought with them to Bethlehem and which, as has been shown in recent research, do indeed have antiseptic and anti-inflammatory properties.

We are also witnessing renewed interest in spices such as cinnamon,

---

[14] Lynn White, *Cultural Climates and Technological Advances in the Middle Ages*, vol.II, (Viator, 1971), p. 174.

appreciated by the Greeks and Romans for their curative powers.

Recent research reveals that almost 80 per cent of the medicinal plants used by our ancestors were truly beneficial. It is therefore perhaps not surprising that the French government has finally authorised the sale of a number of herbal remedies in pharmacies; the latter will benefit financially, for by the end of the 1980s France was already consuming 40,000 tonnes per year, or three times the total for the 1960s. On the other hand, this return to past medicinal practice brings little profit to the pharmaceutical industry.

One of the most striking examples of the industry's negative approach is the rejection of a miracle treatment for burns. This is sodium hypochlorite solution, similar to the formula used by a Paris pharmacist, Labarraque, in 1826 to prevent putrefaction in catgut factories and which proved very satisfactory in the treatment of infected wounds. It was used during the American Civil War, to prevent gangrene after amputation of frost-bitten limbs in both civilians and soldiers, and was also widely used during the First World War.

At the beginning of the Second World War, John Bunyan – descendant of the author of *Pilgrim's Progress* – discovered that the use of a stronger solution of sodium hypochlorite followed by bathing with a weaker isotonic solution was effective not only in combatting infection but for pain-free treatment of serious burns, particularly for pilots injured in the Battle of Britain. He invented what became known as 'the Bunyan Bag', an envelope made of synthetic resin in which to rest the burnt area, protecting it against further infection as it bathed the burns. These bags were used once again by the Royal Navy during the Falklands war in 1982.

In 1979 Bunyan wrote:

> The use of hypochlorite fell into desuetude with the advent of antibiotics and it is only in the last few years that surgeons have realised that antibiotics are not the final answer in the treatment of wounds and burns and, indeed, can often prove dangerous or even fatal. Modern widely-used antiseptics have been shown to be toxic and of limited effectiveness.

Why, unlike the Royal Navy, can the general public not buy this wonderful lotion? No doubt because the pharmaceutical laboratories would not find it profitable.

The industry does however sell one product, Milton, for sterilising babies' feeding bottles, which consists of the same ingredients as household bleach, but diluted with one per cent of hypochlorite of sodium; this solution is also a remarkable remedy for burns.

Although alternative medicines can be beneficial, it would be wrong to disregard the advantages of traditional medicine, and in particular irresponsible not to have children vaccinated – a very dangerous modern trend.

Nor should it be believed that alternative medicine is always harmless or lacking in side effects.

> Some of these are relatively trivial. Juniper can cause diarrhoea and camomile and yarrow can produce rashes, but broom, for example, may induce abortion and comfrey and coltsfoot have been linked with inducing cancer. Incorrect manipulation by healers may damage joints and acupuncture can lead to severe internal bleeding and carries with it the risk of disease transmission from infected needles.[15]

Legislation against vaccines

As progress in conventional medicine is increasingly restricted we may, whether we like it or not, have to turn more frequently to alternative medicine. The restrictive attitude of the FDA in the medical domain has already been mentioned, but in the USA today there is an even greater limiting factor, already mentioned in chapter 1. This is the increasingly strict body of laws of liability which act as a brake not only on the industry but on medicine itself. I mentioned above that more than 95 per cent of the cost of a child's vaccine represented the insurance cost: this exorbitant 95 per cent tax affects every one of us.

Between 1965 and 1985 an ever-increasing number of US vaccine manufacturers simply gave up their research and production.

> By 1986 the United States had to depend on sole suppliers for vaccines against polio, rubella, measles, mumps and rabies. Not long ago there were eight manufacturers of a whooping-cough vaccine, today there is only one. For a brief time it looked as if the US might be down to zero and the Center for Disease Control declared a crisis and began stockpiling emergency supplies ... Companies that get out of risky areas such as the vaccine business tend to stay out. Today only two major companies – Merck and Lederle – are investing serious money in vaccine research.[16]

The US is no longer the world leader either in manufacture or in distribution of vaccines. And since no other industrial nation has taken over this task, the human race as a whole is the loser. One hope still remains, however – that we shall see the developing countries taking up the challenge.

---

[15] Dr Joe Collier, *The Health Conspiracy*, (London, 1982), p. 24.

[16] Peter W. Huber, *Liability Law: The Enemy of Innovation*, Policy Forum, The Cato Institute.

Do we still need Scientists?

Although the irrational forces of the counterculture which launched its attack on science in the 1960s have not yet succeeded in introducing astrology into astronomy or alchemy into the chemist's laboratory, they have succeeded in toppling the men of science who had held their exalted positions since 1945. Their laboratories were to be the fulfilment of Louis Pasteur's hopes in the nineteenth century, 'Temples of the Future and of Common Welfare'.

Certain twentieth-century scholars have realised that these irrational forces were the same as those which have appeared regularly throughout history, undermining reason and progress. An article in the US journal Fortune in March 1971, headed 'The Senseless War on Science', claimed that the counterculture had turned away from scientific reality towards 'the arts and handicrafts and a return to nature à la Rousseau and revel in astrology, drugs, and those eastern mysticisms that for centuries have held whole continents impoverished'.

Within the scientific world the attack on science and the attention given to certain forms of mysticism – even in a university such as Cambridge – have stimulated students to attend religious revivalist meetings. It may be coincidence, but mathematics students form the majority of devotees of this mysticism – mathematics being the branch of science least directly concerned with everyday realities.

The alarming aspect is that some professors are influenced by this modern day irrational state of mind. A distinguished professor of mathematics and physics, John Gerald Taylor, who according to Who's Who is a member of the most celebrated scientific institutions of Europe and the USA, has written books on the phenomena of the paranormal.

In *Superminds* the physicist Taylor tells us how spoons can be bent solely through the force of an individual's willpower. The man he describes is Uri Geller, watched by millions on television. Science appeared defeated by not having reckoned with mysterious powers to be found within us, but Professor Taylor, who should have been on his guard because Geller was known to be a conjurer, finally acknowledged that he had been deceived.

An astrophysicist known to the author, one of many with unassailable professional records, wrote to him in a personal letter:

A number of biologists are abandoning the paths of reason and logic in order to test approaches which contradict achievements in this field and call upon techniques such as premonition or telepathy. A relativity physicist, Olivier Costa de Beauregard, seized on the paradox EPR (Einstein, Podewslsky, Rosen), one of the burning issues in modern theoretical physics, which he placed at the heart of a well-constructed intellectual edifice, but which none the less included telepathy and psycho-kinetics.

Not only have attacks on science reduced the number of students in science faculties, but such attacks have led to unemployment among young researchers because some western governments – particularly in the UK – have appreciably reduced investment in non-military scientific research since the early 1970s. This state of affairs explains, but does not excuse, either the rivalry in laboratories or the malpractices that are slowly coming to light. Governments sometimes seek to justify the high proportion of funds granted for military research by the prospect of subsequent benefits for civil industry: these claims have turned out to be unfounded.

Loss of creativity with increasing age

Another factor in the decline of science in the west is the increasing average age of researchers in OECD countries, particularly the USA. All OECD nations which have studied the question have established that the average age of research workers rose during the 1970s. In the USA, for example, the average age of members of the faculties of science and engineering rose from forty-one in 1968 to forty-four in 1974.

Interesting studies carried out by Japanese scholars, methodically examining western science since the beginning of the sixteenth century, have demonstrated the influence of age on creativity.[1] Italy's great period of creativity lasted from 1550 to about 1610, that of England from Newton's day, 1660, to 1730, that of France from 1770 to 1830 and that of Germany from 1810 to 1920. The decline in excellence in each of these nations coincided with a rise in the average age of scholars. Scientific creativity in the USA began in the second quarter of the twentieth century, but by the early 1980s it was already on the decline.

The decline of Hellenistic, Islamic and medieval science

For a better understanding of phenomena favouring western creativity today it is interesting to look at past cultures which have evolved in

---

[1] *Japanese Studies in the History of Science*, (Tokyo, 1962).

ways similar to our own. Historians of science have often noted correlations between the decline of science and the rise of the occult and irrational. The laws governing the evolution of science are very different from those which govern the development of technology; technology develops ahead of science, while science continues to make advances when technology has reached a plateau of achievement. At the end of the cycle technology survives, but science fades away.

The irrational forces which were to shake and undermine Hellenistic science, for example, appeared during the third century BC but were only to have a decisive effect at the beginning of the Christian era. It was at the end of the second century AD that the impetus of Greek science finally faded and died.

A number of cultural influences from within the Hellenistic world were responsible for this withering. They included the Stoics and the Epicureans who seem to have discouraged scientific research. The important science historian George Sarton suggests that the Stoics had the most disastrous influence on science because:

> they indulged in occultism, they favoured divination. Their acceptance and fostering of astrology were a real betrayal of truth as men of science understand it ... The Stoics ... jeopardised its progress.[2]

Other irrational but even more powerful forces were rooted in eastern religions such as the Gnostic and Hermetic movements.

> The qualities required to arrive at 'knowledge' are no longer intelligence, observation and objectivity but a pure heart, a blind faith, not to mention amongst the activists of these sects a frenzied imagination ... Science is dealt a direct blow: astrology competes with astronomy, alchemy extinguishes the first stirring of chemistry, botany becomes degraded in a pharmacopoeia encumbered with ridiculous recipes, zoology in a collection of 'wonders', each one as fantastic as the next.[3]

What happened to Hellenistic science and what is taking place today in the western world happened in Islamic science in the twelfth and thirteenth centuries. Its most flourishing period was in the ninth, tenth and eleventh centuries 'when science was encouraged on a scale unequalled since the days of Alexandria'.[4] It was a time when 'the patronage of scientists was a deliberate policy of the State represented by the Caliph or the government ... the State enabled scientists and engineers to spend all their time on research and writing'.[5]

[2] George Sarton, *A History of Science*, (Cambridge, Mass. 1959), p. 610.

[3] J.D. Bernal, *Science in History*, (Harmondsworth, 1964), vol 1, p. 273.

[4] Donald R. Hill and Aymed Y al-Hassan, *Islamic Technology*, (Cambridge, 1986), p. 12.

[5] Ibid.

Only a few of the Islamic scholars who made advances in science can be named here – Al-Kindi, in the ninth century, who classified science and wrote on mineralogy, geology, physics, pharmacology and medicine; Al-Alhazen (c. 965–1039), whose work on optics was translated into Latin including a solution to a problem which still bears his name;[6] Al-Biruni (973-1048), who wrote 150 works on mathematics, astronomy and geography and who always tested his conclusions by observation and experiment;[7] or Al-Khawismi (c. AD 875) whose name lies behind the term 'algorithm' and who was also responsible for Islamic – and hence western – algebra.

In the second half of the twelfth century, however, the guardians of Islamic law discarded virtually all the philosophy introduced into their culture three centuries earlier when much of the Greek philosophy and science had been translated into Arabic. As the theologians seized hold of Islam the great surge in Arab science which had taken the world forward began to ebb. By the beginning of the thirteenth century the occult sciences had found a home in Islam.

> It was then that magic blended with piety ... talismans will no longer consist only of magic squares, mysterious drawings and chanting figures, but will blend these strange figures with respectable Koranic texts ... Drawn up as a doctrinal corpus ... they helped to destroy Islam's logic, austerity and universality.[8]

However, it was not only in the Hellenistic and Islamic worlds that science fell from pre-eminence; this also happened in India and in China. Closer at hand, in medieval Europe, science took off in the twelfth century with the aid of Greek and Islamic scientific texts translated by teams of scholars including Christians, Jews and Moslems in cities such as Toledo in Spain.

Great scientists such as Robert Grosseteste appeared in the first half of the thirteenth century. He was to write commentaries on Aristotle's physics; he considered it impossible to understand the world of physics without mathematics, basing his approach on his notions of metaphysics and the nature of the real. He made a study of optical lenses. The name of Roger Bacon is associated with the origins of experimental science; his name appears in chapter 1 with his prediction of the automobile, the submarine and the aircraft. In 1269 Pierre de Maricourt wrote an epoch-making book on magnetism which remained preeminent for 300 years, superseded only in 1600 by William Gilbert, physician to Queen

---

[6] Ibid., p. 22.

[7] Ibid., pp. 20–5.

[8] Armand Abel 'La place des sciences occultes dans la décadence' in *Classicisme et Déclin culturel dans l'histoire de l'Islam*, (Paris, 1977, pp. 306r8.

Elizabeth I. In 1377 Nicolas Oresme, Bishop of Lisieux, revived the concept that the earth rotated daily on its axis and wrote treatises on mathematics and cosmology as well as refutations of magic and astrology. He lived in the declining years of the Middle Ages, when irrational forces were once again expanding. Growing mysticism in Europe at that time aroused great interest in witchcraft and the occult sciences, geomancy, hydromancy, necromancy and alchemy.

In this atmosphere medieval science withered away, as had happened in earlier times; the distinguishing feature here, however, was the revival of science two centuries later which was to be one of the major events in history, the Scientific Revolution. The cycle of western culture has thus seen two scientific cycles.

Nuclear power, the new factor in the cycle

The present day scientific cycle is however very different from its predecessors because we have created a technology capable of destroying the whole world – the atom bomb. There is nothing in history which can compare even remotely with nuclear power, for gunpowder is a relatively merciful means of destruction compared with the bomb. Nor is there anything like the nuclear wastes which will remain with us, or with our descendants if we have any, for thousands of years. It is terrifying to see our rulers making their plans only in terms of generalities and not of the civilisations which will survive us.

Is it not alarming to learn that a Head of State, a believer in astrology, was in a position to press the nuclear button and create a holocaust by following the indications of his horoscope? Unbelievable, perhaps, but true. We were living under this threat when Ronald Reagan was President of the USA, for he consulted a San Francisco astrologer, Nicky Michael, about all his decisions and moves; she even made him sign a treaty (the IMF treaty in 1987) at 1.33 pm because his horoscope recommended this exact moment. In 1988 Donald Regan, the former Chief of Staff, revealed that the calendar on his desk was colour-coded to show which days were or were not suitable for Ronald Reagan to travel. It may be no coincidence that this President came from California, where the alternative culture was born and developed.

The nuclear risk had naturally been discussed for many years, but the role of scientists and their responsibilities in this area was too often neglected. It is true that there had been public statements in the past stating that nuclear power was opening the way to mass death and that scientists were responsible for this; but such statements were rare.

Writing in the journal *Nature* the US scientist Jamie Love asked for 'a dialogue about the morality of German weapons science, an issue of professional importance for certain readers – those who work in arms manufacturing – and a matter of life and death for all of us ...' Love went on to question whether:

> scientists and engineers should not be held responsible for nuclear, chemical and biological weapons. Do they defend their actions by claiming 'I only build them, I don't use them' ... and expect their respective governments to shoulder the moral responsibility? It is perhaps not too late to teach our graduate students and peers that it is wrong to research and develop more efficient means to murder and destroy.[9]

Scientists have committed crimes against humanity, and are still committing them, but the scientific community rarely meets to discuss the ethics of their current or proposed research. Scientists are often seen as the priests of our time, but although priests of all faiths have traditionally been bound by a moral code, the priests of science are definitely not similarly bound.

Fortunately voices are being raised world-wide in protest against this divine right which scientists have claimed for themselves. In his excellent book on the alternative future, Pierre Drouin recalls the famous introductory lecture given at the Collège de France on 3 November 1967, when Jacques Monod sanctified knowledge.

> The sole aim, the supreme value, the sovereign good in the ethics of knowledge, does not lie – we must confess – in the happiness of mankind, still less in worldly power or comfort, nor even in the Socratic 'Know thyself' – it is objective knowledge itself. I think it must be said that this ethic must be systematised, removed from all social, moral or political consequences, that it must be publicised and taught, for, as the creator of the modern world, knowledge is the only factor to match it. It should not be concealed that this is a severe and restricting ethic which, although it respects man's search for knowledge, defines a value which is superior to man himself...[10]

Drouin goes on to comment, very accurately, that 'this represents a desperate deification of knowledge ... Man deserving respect because he loves knowledge (as if he had no right to respect purely as a "person"), knowledge representing a greater virtue than human life, thus justifying every form of biological experiment'.[11]

In the UK, Sir Douglas Hague, former chairman of the Economic and

---

[9] 'Scientists' attitudes to weapons', letter in *Nature* from Jamie Love of the department of Biochemistry and Molecular Biology at Louisiana State University, New Orleans, 27 October 1988.

[10] Pierre Drouin, *L'Autre Futur*, (Paris, 1989), p. 22.

[11] Ibid, pp. 22–3.

Social Research Council, told scientists at the 1989 British Association for the Advancement of Science that 'scientists believe in their own divine right' to appropriate society's resources because of their calling, and added that 'society has the right to make scientists accountable for what they do and how much they spend doing it' and that 'politicians also have the right to know if the demand for increased expenditure is really justified'.[12] Hague suggested that what scientists lacked most was humility.

In the USA too the same suggestion can be heard even within the scientific community itself. The President of Stanford University in California, Donald Kennedy, delivering the keynote speech at the American Association for the Advancement of Science in 1985, took aim at 'the scientists who contributed to a public mistrust of science by exaggerating its usefulness'. He suggested that scientists should stop claiming that scientific advances would make the USA more economically competitive. He criticised the popular misconception that good science demands a deep purse and suggested that researchers should approach the public with more humility and gratitude, for it is the public which has created a society capable of supporting research. In conclusion he asserted that 'the argument by which investments in research improve the economic prosperity of certain regions was the way to convert science to the haggling and horse trading of a public project'.[13]

Have we reached the end of the scientific revolution?

That the President of one of the famous US universities could link haggling and horse trading with science begs a question: is our glorious scientific revolution coming to an inglorious end?

Perhaps one of the first scientists to query the limits of present day science is Arnold Kramish, a nuclear scientist who worked on the famous Manhattan Project to create the first atom bomb. He wrote:

> The time has come to re-examine science advocacy, its costs and benefits to mankind. This could be a long-term task for an international commission resulting in short-term cost-benefits for the global community and long-term knowledge benefits for mankind.[14]

As the scientific revolution becomes conscious of its age, Arnold Kramish very naturally turns to the first theoretician of science, Francis Bacon

---

[12] 'Selfish scientists expect pennies from heaven', *New Scientist*, 16 September 1989.

[13] 'The overselling of American science', *New Scientist*, 21 January 1989.

[14] Taken from a memorandum 'The Limits of Science and High Technology' from Arnold Kramish, December 1988.

who, in the seventeenth century, announced that 'Knowledge is Power'. Kramish continues:

> If Francis Bacon had ever reflected on the cost of scientific research in his day – and there is no indication that he did – he would not have narrowed the expectation that he could afford to know everything. ... But even Bacon would blanch at the modern-day costs of probing all of the ultimate secrets of nature. That quest is ultimately doomed because every new scientific discovery uncovers new unknowns forming more branches of the tree of knowledge to be explored. Mankind in only the past decades has finally reached the impasse dictated by resource limitations in the quest for basically unlimited scientific knowledge.[15]

Like many philosophers and science fiction writers of later ages, Bacon had in fact no perception whatsoever that knowledge, particularly scientific knowledge, could be prohibitively costly. As we move closer to the year 2000 we are increasingly faced with excessively costly super-projects in science. The titles give them away – superconductors, supersynchrotons, super-computers; and since this comes at a time when national budgets are feeling under strain, many such projects may never see the light of day.

The Superconducting Super Collider (SSC), a high-energy particle accelerator designed to explore the ultimate constituents of matter, is but one of these colossal projects. Some ten thousand superconducting magnets are to accelerate protons close to the speed of light, to smash them with a violence rivalling that of the Big Bang. The SSC tunnel would be nearly 90 kilometres in diameter, large enough to go right round New York City. The accelerator would be sufficiently powerful to discover the latest Holy Grail of particle physics, the Higgs boson. It would either find it or not, which would lead on to fresh theories. The US Congress voted not to finance the project in October 1993, on the basis that it was uneconomic to spend nearly $8m on nothing more than opening the way to fresh theories.

An end to the Golden Age of Science

Following a conference organised by the Ditchley Foundation in July 1989 on the future of science and technology, John Maddox, director of *Nature*, wrote in an article 'Is there a future for Research?':

> Whatever happened to the golden age of science when research was assured of unstinted support? Has public enchantment with the research enterprise melted away and, if so, why? Is the pace of inno-

---

[15] Ibid.

vation now so much more rapid than that of human evolution by natural selection that bewilderment is unavoidable?[16]

After much reading and thinking we are not sure where the answer lies.
Have we expected too much of science and technology? Were we right
to spend so much public money since the Second World War on so many
scientific projects which have failed? And as the scientists' halo fades, we
can perhaps reflect on the fact that scientists have not yet been able to
solve the mysteries of the origins of life and will probably never do so.

A better understanding of the fallibility of science and scientists can be
derived from reading what the French philosopher and scientist Edgar
Morin says after long years of considering such problems:

> Following Newton it was thought that scientific theory would provide
> the certainty that religion no longer offered. Scientific theories are cer-
> tainly based on verified data and thereby become proven, but their
> own scientific nature is one of fallibility and not proven like theories.
> Whitehead, Popper and Kuhn have each in their own way shown that
> scientific theories are fragile and not permanent. The permanent refu-
> tation of scientific theory is the deciding feature distinguishing it from
> ideological or religious dogma which is, to the believer's eyes,
> irrefutable ... Modern science has thereby opened up dialogue with
> uncertainty and inadequacy.[17]

In discussing theses on science and ethics Morin wrote:

> We must realise that science and reason have no fortunate mission to
> operate for the welfare of mankind, they have ambivalent powers
> over the future development of our humanity.[18] ... Today we have
> reached the era of 'Big Science', techno-science with colossal powers ...
> now there is a hitherto unknown interaction between research and
> power. Many scientists believe they can avoid the problems posed by
> this interaction, believing in a difference between science on the one
> hand and technology on the other, and between both of them and
> politics. These are the scientists who say: 'Science is excellent, it is
> moral. Technology is ambivalent, like Aesop's language. Politics is
> bad, and bad developments in science are the result of politics.' Such a
> view ignores not only actual cross-currents between the three but also
> ignores the fact that scientists are actors on the stage of military poli-
> tics and of nations.[19] ... thus scientific practice itself leads us into

---

[16] John Maddox, Nature, 20 July 1989.

[17] Edgar Morin Science avec conscience, 'Points Sciences' series, (Paris), p. 213.

[18] Ibid., p. 115.

[19] Ibid., p. 116–7.

complete irresponsibility and ignorance.[20]

Rare indeed are the scientists who face up to their responsibilities. They do exist, however, and we should acknowledge them. A group of French scientists, of whom the most famous is Jacques Testard – who created France's first test-tube baby – issued a manifesto in 1989 which faced up fully to the end of the golden age of science and the problems which scientists and the world of today must confront. He offers suggestions on how scientists should think and act.

Mastering Science

The desire to understand the world today has been overtaken by the need to exploit it. Scientific results and advances are for the most part produced within institutions whose ultimate aims are technological. The direction in which research, whether 'fundamental' or 'applied', proceeds is governed by economic, social, health-related or military considerations.

This orientation cannot be ignored by research workers and society has the right to pass judgment on it ... Thus unless science can be brought under control it represents a serious risk to the environment, to mankind and to individuals ... In the name of scientific truth, life is reduced to its measurable aspects. The increasingly narrow specialisation of scientists encourages their shortsightedness as to their role in society and creates insurmountable barriers between the different scientific disciplines.

We believe that clear thinking is more important than efficiency and the direction of research more important than the speed with which it is accomplished. We believe that reflection should precede any scientific project rather than following innovation. We believe that this reflection is essentially more philosophical than technical and should take place across interdisciplinary barriers and include the whole of society.[21]

Confession of a nuclear engineer

On the day of his retirement in January 1982, Admiral Rickover, one of the nuclear military engineers who created the *Nautilus*, the first nuclear submarine, gave evidence to the US Congress. To Senator Proxmire who called him a 'national monument', Rickover responded that for him the risk of nuclear radiation inspired a certain philosophy.

Until about two billion years ago it was impossible to have any life on earth ... there was so much radiation you couldn't have any life – fish

---

[20] Ibid., p. 119.

[21] Manifesto, 'Maîtriser la science', *Le Monde*, 19 March 1988.

or anything. Gradually the amount of radiation reduced and made it possible for some life to begin ... Now, when we go back to using nuclear power we are creating something which nature tried to destroy to make life possible. Then you might ask why I built nuclear ships? They were an necessary evil. I would sink them all.[22]

Although used to his straightforward speaking the members of Congress could not believe their ears and asked him to repeat what, coming from an expert and an officer, seemed as absurd as desertion in the face of the enemy.[23]

Admiral Rickover responded, 'I am not proud of the part I have played in it. I did it because it was necessary for the safety of the country. That's why I am such a great exponent of stopping this nonsense of nuclear war.'[24] ... And when the senator asked him what he thought of nuclear war, he replied, 'I think that we will probably destroy ourselves, so what difference will it make? Some new species will come up that might be wiser'.[25]

Better late than never. But would not this confession have had greater impact earlier in his career when he was first seized with doubts over the (guilty) role he was playing in promoting nuclear technology? This brings us to another question. How many scientists working in military or civilian nuclear installations have a sense of guilt? Many, we hope; but few if any are those who at any level, responsible for crimes against humanity, make public confessions like that of Admiral Rickover. Not only should they sign the oath referred to earlier, but they should read and meditate on the confession of one of their own distinguished peers.

Thought should come before research

They should take seriously the example of Jacques Testard, who was instrumental in drafting the manifesto 'Towards a better control of Science'. Testard took the unprecedented decision to do just that, of reflecting in advance on the consequences and risks which might arise from his research. Since 1986 he has abandoned his work on human embryos and has redirected his research to animal embryos. Pushing his ideology to its logical extreme he is giving up all research on animal embryos immediately he feels that the results may be applied to the study of human embryos.

Jacques Testard's courageous attitude has clearly upset the scientific

---

[22] Evidence of Admiral Rickover to the Joint Economic Committee, US Senate, Washington, *Stenographic Transcripts AGE-Federal Reporters*, 28 January 1982.

[23] *New York Review of Books*, 18 March 1982, p. 19.

[24] J.J. Salomon, 'Science, Guerre et Paix', *Economica*, 1989, 25.

[25] Ibid., 25.

community, which considers that to some extent it constitutes a threat to the 'divine right' of researchers. As in any religion, a heretic is appearing who questions certain fundamental beliefs and seeks to instal a new ethic. I hope that we are witnessing the end of the era of the all-powerful scientist, free to create nuclear power and free to endanger the future of humanity. Let us hope that new generations of researchers will hold to Testard's ethic and will resist the dangers of genetic research. It can never be repeated too often that much of the danger lies in the disinformation disseminated by the scientific world. We learn increasingly often that scientists have withheld information on nuclear leaks; in the medical world we are discovering today that the success rate of *in vitro* fertilisation is by no means what was originally stated. In an article co-written by Testard, we read that, faced with the disinformation which is the norm in this area, the global average rate of birth per attempt is undoubtedly very much less than seven per thousand.[26] The author of the article complained that 'accidents are only mentioned in whispers in conference corridors' and that there is virtually never any mention of 'the great number of multiple pregnancies with their complications miscarriages, prematurity, caesarian births'.[27]

Such problems result not only in physical suffering for the women concerned, they are also the cause of psychological trauma.

Some women remain heartbreakingly sterile after fifteen attempts while others give birth to triplets, quadruplets, or even quintuplets, generally receiving no supplementary help with the subsequent immense family problems. Further, many of these babies weigh no more than 1500 grammes at birth: many will die young and others remain physically and mentally handicapped.

Such disasters pose the question of scientific responsibility. In the UK the microbiologist John Beringer, chairman of a new committee for the control of genetic engineering, has gone so far as to ask if those who disobey the directives of the ethical committees should not be prosecuted and possibly sent to prison. He fears that university researchers may be better at avoiding regulation than those in industry ... And in fact in June 1990, only a few months after his appointment, John Beringer learned that scientists at St Bartholomew's Hospital in London had been discovered undertaking illegal experiments.

The matter at risk is this thirst for knowledge, this worship of knowledge lauded by Jacques Monod. Writing in the journal *La Recherche*, the lawyer Bernard Edelman quoted Nietszche, who placed sacrifice at the

---

[26] Nicole Athea, Geneviève Desai, Laurence Gavarine, François Laborie, Joachim Marcus-Stieff, Jacques Testard and Anne-Marie de Vilaine, 'Procréatique et désinformation', *Le Monde*, 17 December 1987.

[27] Ibid.

heart of western reasoning: 'Knowledge is transformed in us into a pas-
sion which no sacrifice can alarm and which has at its foundation only
one fear, that of personal death ... The passion for knowledge may perhaps bring about the death of humanity itself.' Edelman continued, 'we
may have become a humanity which sacrifices itself not on the altar of
truth but on the altar of knowledge'.[28]

What we should find particularly alarming in this excessive liberty
granted to scientists is the fact that some of them are fraudulent. In
recent years the press has revealed some of the great names of science
who have betrayed us: Cyril Burt, John Darsee, William McBride, David
Baltimore (a Nobel Prize-winner), Vizwa Jit Gupta, Robert Gallo. Writing
in *Le Monde*, Doctor Escoffier-Lambiotte headed an article, '1983, the
cheats were here':

> But the very image of cheating is a severe blow to that of science,
> where terminology is so often presented as an argument of austerity
> and integrity. Should we join with Spengler in seeing learned fraud as
> a sign of the decadence of civilisations?[29]

The doctor very judiciously quoted Oswald Spengler, author of *Decline of
the West* which I quoted in chapter 6 'We will not escape the law of
cycles', for the critical problems facing science today are somewhat similar to those of past societies which lived through the decline of sciences
in their civilisation.

A gulf has appeared in the west between society and science. To quote
Hans Zacher, chairman of the important Max Planck Company in
Munich which is engaged in fundamental research, 'Society no longer
trusts science,'[30] and he exposes 'the dilemma confronting science: either
to give up research and thereby retrieve public confidence, or to continue at all costs on the present path and see faith in science continue to
drop'.[31] In a *Sciences et Avenir* editorial Marie-Jeanne Hussel also posed
the problem:

> Should we let the possible risks of malpractice or excess in research
> continue? Or should we ban research with the risk of definitively clos-
> ing the door on techniques which might one day be useful to humani-
> ty? Some proclaim their confidence in the ethics of researchers; others
> consider that scientists should no longer make their own decisions.[32]

---

[28] Bernard Edelman, *La Recherche*, September 1991, 1065.

[29] Dr Escoffier-Lambiotte, '1983: les tricheurs étaient parmi nous', *Le Monde*, 23 January
1984.

[30] Barbara Bachtler, 'Society no longer trusts science', *Scientific European*, October 1990, 8.

[31] Ibid., 8.

[32] Marie-Jeanne Hussel, 'Bioéthique: faut-il une loi?', *Sciences et Avenir*, 1990.

France has a law now, the Huriet Law of 20 December 1988, concerning the 'protection of persons offering themselves for biomedical research' and a legislative decree in force since 23 September 1990 which aims to establish a new ethic in this dangerous domain; it also seeks to introduce 'society' into decisions of scientific research. But:

> It is not the rare 'representatives' of civil society in session in committees behind closed doors, nor two or three days a year of national ethics, which will ensure true democratic participation in ethical decisions and the social control of biomedical progress. Rather than introducing secrecy it would be better to organise information and favour the broadest participation in ethical debates.[33]

Bernard Edelman had other reservations on this law. He saw in it 'an extraordinary edifice of financial, scientific and clinical interests where the individual is by turns, depending on the circumstances, experimented on and recompensed for having 'lent' his body – or his disease – to research'. Further, 'Indubitably, this law brings us into the marketplace'.[34]

To avoid the bargainings of the 'market economy' and the possible shortcomings, we must look to Germany and pay homage to this nation which is the first in the world to protect the human embryo. They have introduced a law forbidding surrogate pregnancy, determining the sex of a child before birth except in cases of severe genetic disease, insemination with the sperm of a dead man, the creation of embryos specifically for research purposes and the preservation of fertilised eggs. The law also forbids the graft of hereditary genes and the creation of identical human beings (clones) or hybrids with animals (chimeras). This law took effect on 1 January 1991.

---

[33] Bernard Edelman, op. cit., 1057.
[34] Ibid., 1057.

CHAPTER
8

The Relentless Cycles of History

Despite its distinctive features our civilisation has evolved like all its pre-decessors. No culture has ever believed that it will suffer the same fate as all others. Our way of life resembles that of Apollinaris, the Roman scholar who, some years before the fall of Rome in AD 476, was blind to the approaching end of that civilisation even after the Vandals had sacked Rome in AD 455. The Barbarians occupied the whole of Gaul except for the central part now known as the Auvergne, where Apollinaris owned a magnificent house beside Lake Aydat.

It is simultaneously fascinating, instructive and painful to read the 147-odd letters which Apollinaris despatched to many correspondents before his death around AD 486. Up to the age of forty, his life was com-fortable and light hearted; he was a pleasant and kind hearted man, dis-tinguished, witty, and highly cultivated. His culture, however, was entirely literary, Rome-centred and backward-looking. He had a taste for fine language and valued the mastery of form above all; in modern days he would have been passionately interested in linguistics and liter-ary criticism.

The detailed description of his villa of Avitacus near Clermont-Ferrand, with its wide view, its pool and airy rooms, might nowadays apply to that of a prosperous French or Californian businessman. Those who live in such houses are well protected from the daily life of more modest men and from the fast-approaching storm. Apollinaris wrote:

> My family and I are living in sweet harmony ... To the west there is a steep escarpment ... to the south-west a bath by the foot of a rock cov-ered in wood ... hot water reaches it through lead piping ... In the bath-house the day is perfect ... next to it there is a rest-room ... It has no obscene paintings, no shameful liberties [the Romans of the Decadent period were Christian and prudish] To the outside, on the east of the house, there is a swimming pool ... we go there when we come out of the hot baths ... and into the winter living room and a small dining room from which you can see almost the whole of the lake ... you can enjoy the pleasures of the table and of a delightful view at the same time ... It is wonderful to hear the midday chirping of the crickets and the croaking of the frogs in the evening, the honk-

ing of the swans and geese as the night falls, the cock crowing in the small hours and the cry of the rooks greeting the dawn.[1]

When I am in Provence for the summer I cannot help thinking of this letter. In 1961 the neighbouring village had one swimming pool; today the *commune* has 700. How could one fail to compare them to the Roman baths of the end of the Empire?

None the less, the idyllic description of life at Avitacus reveals some of the economic problems which were already affecting the Roman Empire, particularly concerning commercial transactions and communications. The walls of his villa have no marbles 'from Paris, or from Carytos or Proconissos, not from Phrygia, Numidia or Sparta ... fulgurite stones of Ethiopian rock and precipice, of which the purple colour does nothing to conceal the modesty of our presence'.[2] Although the imperial postal system was still functioning, the famous Roman roads were less and less well maintained and loads of marble could not now be taken along the deteriorating tracks. The villa Avitacus was built of local stone.

The tone of Apollinaris's letters changed in about 470. He finally accepted the truth and acknowledged that the idyllic world of his descriptions existed, in effect, only in his imagination. Rome was crumbling. Very soon freedom of expression would be restricted; Apollinaris hesitated to write letters which might be intercepted. What he could not know, naturally, was that the Roman empire in the East was to undergo a revival and to survive for another thousand years. The coinage of Byzantium was to become the 'dollar' of the High Middle Ages.

The self-satisfaction of a superiority complex

In time the economy of Byzantium deteriorated. Its economic decline stemmed from a phenomenon seen in every society at the peak of its powers: the combined superiority and self-satisfaction complex. Self-satisfaction and the will to change are two incompatible attitudes. As Carlo Cipolla wrote:

> The more a mature empire is part of its natural heritage, the more emotionally difficult it is for its people to change to new modes of doing things, under the pressure of external competition and growing difficulties. Many would feel deeply that to undergo such change would be like admitting defeat. Then change, which could be the only hope of survival, becomes ironically equated with surrender.[3]

---

[1] *Sidonius, Poems and letters*, translated by W.B. Anderson (London and Cambridge, Mass. 1836), vol. I, letter II, p. 429.

[2] Ibid.

[3] Carlo Cipolla, *The Economic Decline of Empires*, (London, 1970), p. 11.

We are witnessing this phenomenon today in Europe and the USA, where it seems difficult to accept the idea that it may be necessary to change ways of working and of thinking in order to return to economic growth.

Society creates institutions which are then extremely difficult to develop, and conservative elements use these institutions to protect their privileges and maintain the status quo. Minorities conscious of the need for change always experience great difficulties in successfully overthrowing the bastions of conservatism, while trade guilds and unions have tended to resist industrial and social progress throughout history, giving rise to their description as 'managers exploiting a monopoly'.

It was the hidebound institutions of Byzantium which gradually yielded control of trade in the eastern Mediterranean to the Italian city-states. Byzantium suffered from such a powerful superiority complex that she was unable to see these 'western barbarians' capable of supplanting her industry and currency – which was soon to be displaced by the Florentine currency. This coinage, the florin, was subsequently supplanted by the guilders of the Netherlands, which in turn gave way to the pound sterling, then to the dollar, and no doubt to the yen.

Bessarion to the rescue of Byzantium

While Byzantium was living out her final years, however, there was a determination to slow down her decline. The unusual feature here was that the effect of rejuvenation was based on development and technical knowledge, the only known example in history of such an attempt, described in masterly fashion by Alexander Keller.[4]

In 1444 the future Cardinal Bessarion drew up a report addressed to Constantine Paleologue who five years later was to become the last Byzantine emperor. At the Council of Florence on the reunion of the Greek and Roman churches in 1439 Bessarion had been astonished by western efficiency, and his report therefore recommended the adoption of certain western innovations which he had observed.

Urging in his report that young men should be sent secretly to the West, Bessarion stressed the significance of hydraulic power in the reduction of manual labour, citing in illustration the use of this form of energy for automatic sawing of wood. He praised hydraulic power for operating 'leather bellows which expand and deflate without being touched ... and which melt and separate metal'.[5] The heat produced by the hydraulic bellows in the blast furnaces was high enough for smelt-

---

[4] A.G. Keller, 'A Byzantine Admirer of Western Progress: Cardinal Bessarion', *Cambridge Historical Journal*, XI (1955).

[5] Ibid., p. 345.

ing, one of the great medieval achievements (although it had already been discovered by the Chinese before the Christian era). According to Bessarion, the new techniques of shipbuilding were among those which should be introduced into the Empire as a matter of priority.

The report also mentioned western arms, without indicating whether this meant the new fire-arms using gunpowder, introduced into Europe about a century earlier and developing rapidly at that time, or conventional weapons.

Bessarion's report was evidently ignored. Such was the resistance to change in fifteenth-century Byzantine society that there was little hope of seeing these recommendations adopted. Even if they had been accepted, it would have been too late to slow the course of history. What is surprising is that the technological reforms which Bessarion wished to introduce into the Empire had been commonplace in the west for at least two centuries. Bessarion does not appear to have realised fully that an industrial revolution had begun next door to Byzantium, but four centuries earlier.

In 1453, less than ten years after the writing of this report, the thousand-year empire of Byzantium ceased to exist.

Ibn Khaldun

Ibn Khaldun, the Arab historian of the fourteenth century and one of the greatest historians of all times, also failed to perceive the existence of an industrial revolution on the other side of the Mediterranean. He simply noted that philosophical sciences were making progress there.

Five hundred years before the West, Ibn Khaldun understood some of the mechanisms which lead to the decline of a society and to its economic crises.

> The inhabitants of towns ... wallow in the enjoyment of their well-being and easy circumstances ... they live in a state of unconcern which has become second nature to them.[6] ... They seek rest, tranquillity and idleness. They undertake the building ... of beautiful monuments and fine houses, they acquire rich clothing. They build palaces and fountains, and indulge in worldly enjoyments. They prefer rest to work and therefore think only of sumptuous garments, refined food, porcelain and tapestries.[7]

The opulence and luxury demand excessive expenditure, leading to increased taxation and serious consequences for the economy and the future of the nation.

---

[6] *Ibn Khaldun, Les Prolegomenes* translated into French by M. de Slane (Paris, 1934), vol. I, p. 213.

[7] Ibid., p. 343.

People overspend, there is a shortage of income and the poor die of hunger; the rich squander their money on luxuries and this state of affairs grows worse from generation to generation until salaries are inadequate. Then the pangs of need begin to make themselves felt.[8] ... As the needs of the government grow, so taxes rise and weigh heavily on the people.[9] ...To attack men by taking their money is to remove the will to work to gain more, for they see that in the end nothing is left to them ... Business becomes disordered and men scatter to seek the means of existence in other countries which they can no longer find at home; the population of the empire decreases, villages are left empty, towns fall into ruin.[10]

No later historian appears to have been similarly intrigued by the decline of a society; the majority have studied the expansion of societies, not their decline. For Ibn Khaldun, 'empires, like individuals, have an existence, a life which is their own; they grow, they reach maturity then they begin to decline'.[11] In studying societies in decline one is struck by their many characteristic similarities.

Although Ibn Khaldun studied the past at great length, he also studied the present with care. Few historians have had such a crowded political life: for nearly fifty years he was closely involved with politics in North Africa, as a high dignitary for various sultans of the period. He was even in touch with two of the most important individuals of his day, Peter the Cruel, the most powerful Christian king in Spain, and Tamerlane, one of history's greatest conquerors.

Towards the end of his life Ibn Khaldun's reputation was such that Tamerlane, who was besieging Damascus, demanded to meet him in his camp at the foot of the city ramparts. Flattered, Ibn Khaldun spent more than a month in his camp early in 1401. During this time he and Tamerlane had many conversations – some of them very animated – on history and the great men of the past, such as Nebuchadnezzar, Alexander the Great and Caesar.

Glubb Pasha

Like a latter-day Tamerlane, Saddam Hussein is interested in the great figures of the past like Nebuchadnezzar, whose palace he has reconstructed, and Saladin, whose name he has used for his personal plane. It may be disturbing to remember that both men captured Jerusalem:

[8] Ibid., p. 344.
[9] Ibid., vol. 1, pp. 92–3.
[10] Ibid., vol. 1, p. 106.
[11] Ibid., vol. 1, p. 349–50.

Nebuchadnezzar in 587 BC and Saladin in AD 1291. Saddam Hussein has named one of his ships *Ibn Khaldun*.

It is certainly no coincidence that Sir John Glubb, better known as Glubb Pasha, who commanded the famous Arab Legion in Jordan from 1939 to 1956, was imbued with the concept of historical cycles. In his remarkable essay, 'The Fate of Empires',[12] published in 1976, he analysed the different stages of an empire's evolution: the Age of Pioneers, the Age of Conquest, the Age of Commerce, the Age of Affluence, the Age of Intellect and the Age of Decadence. In Glubb Pasha's reckoning these cycles lasted for about 250 years on average. I tend to agree with him.

Glubb Pasha wrote that if 'British historians a century ago had devoted serious study to the Arab Empire they could have foreseen everything which has happened in the UK, right up to 1976'.[13] But, as he also wrote, studies of history in the west are generally limited to short periods of national history. National defeats and weaknesses are avoided as topics of study. Certain periods are studied which are seen as privileged, such as ancient Greece or Rome, without relating them properly to other great historic currents. The West is therefore neither aware of its inexorable decline nor preoccupied by it: the history of cycles never appears in the school or university curriculum.

Spengler

As empires decline they gradually invest less and less in the civil sector and more and more in the military sector, convinced that these investments will protect them against the empires in power. In order to balance their external trade they are forced to export their military supplies. In the contemporary world this policy has enabled countries like Iraq to develop weapons which are turned against our own civilisation.

In transferring our advanced technology to developing nations and in teaching them to exploit the primary materials which we need, we are putting ourselves at their mercy. Oswald Spengler, author of the famous *Decline of the West* published in 1918, was the first historian to state that our civilisation would develop like all those which preceded it. He wrote that western technology, which he called Faustian, 'is fast drawing to its inevitable close. It will be eaten up from within like the grand forms of any and every culture. When, and in what fashion, we know not.'[14] Like Ibn Khaldun, he asserted that societies evolve in the same way as nature.

> Cultures, peoples, languages, truths, gods, landscapes bloom and age as the oaks and the stone pines, the blossoms, twigs and leaves – But

---

[12] Glubb Pasha, 'The Fate of Empires', *Blackwood's Magazine*, (December 1976), 484–511.

[13] Ibid., p. 507.

[14] Oswald Spengler, *Man and Technique*, (London, 1992), p. 72.

there is no ageing 'mankind'. Each culture has its own new possibilities of self-expression which arise, ripen, decay and never return ... These cultures, sublimated life essences, grow with the same aimlessness as the flowers of the field.[15]

What particularly drew me to Spengler's work was his profound understanding of the technical and scientific genius of the Middle Ages. He was undoubtedly the first historian to have understood that our society was built on the work of the engineers and scholars of that era. The men of the thirteenth and fourteenth centuries opened the way into the depths of the world of physico-technical problems. They aimed 'not at embracing and unveiling the secrets of the world, but at making them serviceable to definite ends. Hence the advance in mathematical methods, due to the Englishmen Grosseteste (born 1175) and Roger Bacon (born c. 1210) and the Germans Albertus Magnus (born 1153) and Witels (born 1720). Hence too Bacon's experiment "Scientia experimentalis"[16] 'to build a world oneself, to be oneself God, that is the Faustian inventor's dream'.[17]

The Middle Ages/US parallel

The dream of the Faustian seekers finally disturbed the Church. In 1277 the Bishop of Paris, Etienne Tempier, condemned the '219 execrable errors which certain students of the arts faculty have had the temerity to study and to discuss in the schools'. The following year the *Opus Majus* of Roger Bacon was banned. Condemnations acted as a brake on the progress of sciences and reason in Paris. From that period the medieval cycle began its era of decline.

It was succeeded by modern times, in which young nations took on the baton one from another. Italy in the fifteenth century, Portugal and Spain in the sixteenth century, Holland and France in the seventeenth century, England and Germany in the eighteenth and nineteenth centuries, then the USA in the twentieth century, all helped to sustain the momentum: but today the West has no new young nation in reserve and this impetus cannot be sustained. The decline of the West is tragically bound to that of the USA. The incongruous situation which consists of making the USA a nation at the 'tail end of civilisation' is at the origin of the world crisis and explains why economists have been unable to suggest remedies for the world's economic instability.

As my researches led me to study the Middle Ages and the USA I

---

[15] Spengler, *The Decline of the West*, (London, 1926), p. 21.

[16] *Man and Technique*, op. cit., pp. 58–9.

[17] Ibid., p. 59.

increasingly wondered whether the medieval experience could be of benefit to the USA. I was continually struck by the historic parallels which kept arising.

> Pirenne, the great Belgian medievalist, was struck as I have been by the parallels which may be drawn between events of the eleventh and twelfth centuries in Europe and those of the American West in the nineteenth century. Similarities between new towns of the eleventh and twelfth centuries and towns preplanned by American entrepreneurs to follow the development of its railroads are striking. In both cases one finds the emigrants, the pioneer and the self-made man, and both economies arose from freedom to work and free enterprise.[18]

In 1956 I lectured at a Yale conference on the parallels between the development of medieval France and that of the USA. On that occasion I completed the plan above and brought up to date a graph[19] in which cycles are dependent on the close rapport between a nation's psychological drive and its technological development. The graph showed up the decisive influence of psychology on technical development.

During a society's ascendant phase the two curves – of psychological dynamism and of technological development – should be parallel; if it were otherwise, that society would probably cease to develop. As soon as a society enters its mature phase the curve of its psychological drive drops while the curve of technological development falters noticeably. In a period of decline the loss of psychological drive accelerates but that of technology declines more slowly because ageing societies invest abundantly in military technology.

Originally I predicted that the decline of the USA would begin in the 1970s. The year of the turning-point was in fact 1971, the year when Congress refused to vote credits for the SST (the Supersonic Transport – the US version of Concorde). This 'anti-technology' vote represented a complete U-turn in US attitudes to technology. If the year 1947, the year of the Truman doctrine, may be taken as the beginning of the era of American maturity, this era will have lasted for 25 years. The Age of Pericles, sometimes evoked at the White House during Kennedy's presidency, lasted for approximately the same number of years.

When I returned to the USA in 1972, for a seminar at the School of Architecture at the University of Southern California, I discovered the graph which had lain forgotten in a file for 16 years. The evolution which I had predicted was taking place: the decline in civic virtues and crusading spirit, lower growth in GNP, monetary manipulation, growing inflation, resistance to new techniques, etc.

---

[18] Jean Gimpel, *The Medieval Machine*, (London, 1992), p. 242.

[19] Graph published in Gimpel, *The Medieval Machine*, op. cit., pp. 246–7.

The emergence of the counter-culture in the USA, and the Vietnam war, undermined US confidence in the excellence of their country and revealed that US society was evolving as other cultures had done previously. In November 1975 a number of senior US historians met together to consider 'Why did Rome fall? Are we next?'. On the whole the participants answered the second question in the affirmative. A senator from Tennessee remarked that New York, the capital of the American Empire, was on the brink of bankruptcy.

The catastrophe menacing New York led many Americans in the Middle West or Texas to evoke the catastrophes which befell certain cities in the past: Sodom and Gomorrah, Nineveh and Tyre.

During the 1976 Presidential election an historical parallel evoking the decline of the USA suddenly hit the headlines. Henry Kissinger, then Secretary of State, was said to have declared: 'The Russians are Sparta and we are Athens.' It is interesting to note that Kissinger's senior thesis at Harvard had been 'The Meaning of History: Reflexions on Spengler, Toynbee and Kant'.

Since 1991 and the collapse of the Soviet empire this parallel is partially justified, for Athens survived Sparta for a while.

Glubb Pasha had seen clearly what might happen to the USSR when he wrote:

> It is extraordinary how the memory of centuries-old conflicts can suddenly resurface and create regional movements claiming secession or independence. One day this will no doubt happen in the Soviet empire, apparently so monolithic and authoritarian. It is astonishing how such feelings can survive the passage of time.[20]

France's revival

Exceptional circumstances may temporarily break the unfolding of cycles of civilisation. The defeat of 1940, the German occupation, the Liberation, General De Gaulle, the Marshall Plan – these are some of the events which helped to delay France's decline. In other areas certain factors have helped to rejuvenate the nation: appreciable growth in national income and population; modernisation of agriculture; industrialisation; reduced resistance to inventions; competitive 'world-beating' spirit; collective spirit (sport); less hostility towards the young.

This psychological, technological and economic revival in France has enabled French industrialists to adopt the same dynamism and efficiency as US businessmen (pre-1971). But this revival does not indicate that France can escape the inevitable shared decline, since she is part of the

---

[20] Glubb Pasha, op. cit., pp. 498–9.

western world which, as I have indicated, no longer has a 'young nation in reserve'. Moreover she is already affected by the 'counter-culture' affecting the whole of the western world.

Among the reviving factors I mentioned the Marshall Plan, which was a unique phenomenon in world history. No victorious nation had ever hitherto offered financial aid to its impoverished allies nor, still more incredible, had there ever been an offer to reestablish the enemy economy. This factor clearly played a determining role in the rebirth of France, also of the UK, Germany, Italy, and Japan. Thanks to the Plan the standard of living in the nations of the western world and its allies rose considerably.

Today the effects of the Marshall Plan are exhausted and the world is in crisis. No nation is wealthy enough to renew the gesture of the USA at the end of the Second World War.

The west threatened by a Wall Street crash

This is certainly true of the European Community, a giant with feet of clay, threatened by internal dissension as well as by the extreme fragility of the international financial system which rests on a knife-edge. The West has had some difficult years, due to the burden of debt in Third World countries – particularly Brazil – whose failure to repay might have set off a new Wall Street crash and a terrifying economic crisis.

One of the chief reasons for this indebtedness is the disastrous agricultural policy of economists in the Third World and also in the West, ignoring in most cases the links between industry and agriculture. However, history has shown that no country can take off industrially until it has first achieved take-off in its agriculture. The industrial revolution of the Middle Ages could only occur because it had been preceded by an agricultural revolution. The same sequence occurred in England in the eighteenth century. Today, farmers have been allowed (or encouraged) to borrow beyond all reason. Raymond Delatouche, one of the very rare historians with a deep knowledge of agricultural realities, writes:

> Incapable of creating its own funds, agriculture must borrow. The relative reduction in farm prices means that the industry is unable to repay. This fact is obvious in the Third World: its insolvency endangers the world banking system and thereby the industrial world ... It is no less general in the wealthy world: in the United States as in Denmark, France and elsewhere, everywhere the chief claim of agriculture is for debts to be written off.[21]

---

[21] Raymond Delatouche, *La Chrétienté médiévale, un modèle développement*, (Tequi, 1989), p. 144.

Demonstrations by French farmers clearly reflect governmental incomprehension of the laws governing agriculture throughout the world.

Today not only are US farmers overwhelmed by debt but their country is the most heavily debt-burdened in the whole world. In recent years many banks have failed and Wall Street is living very dangerously. It is entirely thanks to the wisdom of one man, Alan Greenspan, named President of the Federal Reserve Bank in July 1987, that crisis was avoided. Learning on his arrival that there was no emergency plan in case of crisis in Wall Street, he immediately had plans drawn up for dealing with any such situation. When shares on Wall Street collapsed one October morning that same year, the Greenspan plan was put into action. The Federal Reserve Bank paid out money to the banks which immediately paid it into Wall Street. The crash was narrowly avoided, which would otherwise have decimated the world's monetary system, with nations, industries and individuals ruined.

We would have been in a situation much more dramatic than that of 1929, for the USA was then a young country capable of recovery – which is no longer the case. We would already be living through the end of our civilisation. But the risk of a Wall Street crash remains.

Consequences for the planet

Attempting to foresee exactly what will happen throughout the five continents is an extremely delicate task because of the large number of unpredictable factors involved.

When I attempted to predict the future of the USA I used many elements of comparison and overall my predictions proved accurate. To foresee the consequences of the collapse of our civilisation is more conjectural, for comparison with past cultures is of limited assistance.

It is not unthinkable that the USA might disunite, the Canadian provinces split up and Quebec finally gain its independence. The European Union could break down and turn into a collection of minorities. One of the major problems facing France will be its nuclear power stations which, abandoned following a catastrophic drop in electricity consumption, will become radioactive ruins. The former West Germany will suffer humiliation as its standard of living is reduced to that of the old East German republic. The UK will become a developing country once more.

Black Africa, where the per capita income has dropped appreciably in recent years under the combined effects of western banks desperate for interest payments and local middle classes desperate for power, will perhaps not suffer too much, for the rupture of economic bonds with the West will entail a return for urban citizens to their recently abandoned rural lives. We shall see export cultures abandoned in favour of traditional ways of life which will enable the people to eat better. Unlike former privileged town dwellers, who will no doubt suffer a drop in their standard of living, the majority of the population will see standards sustained at least, if not actually improving.

In the post-civilisation period the political renaissance of Islam will be confirmed. A Saddam Hussein-type of conqueror will know no limits to his military ambitions; no doubt there will be some nostalgia for 'the good old days'. As with all previous civilisations, we have supplied the means to manufacture weapons of ever-increasing sophistication to all those with whom we have been in contact. Similarly, we have benefited from the military techniques of such as Genghis Khan and Tamerlane. This is the tragic cycle of history. The only difference is that this time, with nuclear power, we are offering them the weapon of final destruction.

The Pacific Basin, which for some years has been the only region in the world to expand economically, will suffer a brief deceleration of its economy after the Wall Street Crash, which may in fact have been triggered by Tokyo, Hong Kong or Singapore. But in the long term the Far East will recover and progressively achieve world economic supremacy equal to that of the west formerly.

A financial and political ORSEC or contingency plan

Yet what can the various nations of the world do today to prevent the disastrous effects of such a crisis? First the nations must face up to such a threat psychologically – which generally does not happen. My article, 'How to help the United States age gracefully',[22] written when I saw the USA in the 1970s evolving as I had predicted, was followed a year later by a conference in Los Angeles[23] which brought together many personalities of the political and economic world to discuss my analysis. The conference decided that the USA and the western world were not suffering from any decline and that there was therefore no point in proposing remedies for non-existent ills. Listening to the speakers I had the impression that I was listening to Apollinaris.

And yet the economic situation in the USA has deteriorated seriously since then. More and more books are brought out, in the USA as well as in Europe, discussing the possibility of a fresh Wall Street crash which would throw the world into economic disaster. These books often evoke the tulipomania in seventeenth-century Holland, the failure of the India

---

[22] Jean Gimpel, 'The Greying of America', *National Review*, 26 November 1976.

[23] The seminar, 'The Future of the West', University of Southern California, 17–19 March 1977.

Company and the South Sea Bubble in England in 1720. Some of these books recall warnings, such as that of the banker Paul M. Warburg who, in March 1929, predicted that a collapse of stock market holdings would lead to an economic depression with consequences affecting the whole nation. The crash came a few months later, in October 1929.

Although many of these works suggest solutions for survival during the crisis – often very useful – there is no suggestion of a contingency plan for our governments. The initiative for setting up emergency measures could be useful in avoiding the worst. In 1952 France established a plan to ensure aid in the case of 'exceptional events' – physical events such as earthquake, fire, flood or leakage of poisonous or radioactive materials. It is drawn up, applied and directed by the *préfet* with the aid of his departmental managers in an operations hall inside the national civilian protection service; it may also be under the management of the *préfet* of the Defence Zone and the Minister of the Interior. This is ORSEC – *Organisation des secours*, or Aid Plan. However, there is unfortunately no ORSEC or contingency plan for dealing with a financial catastrophe which may have disastrous economic and psychological consequences.

It is therefore absolutely essential that all governments establish immediately a financial, economic, social and political ORSEC plan to soften the shock of a collapse in share values, which would strike all nations within a single day.[24] The plan must make it possible to sustain the currency by putting gold reserves and other currencies on the market under very strict measures of exchange control, even if it involves disregarding international monetary agreements. As a house of cards collapses, so banks collapse. Neither cheques nor credit cards will be honoured. But the contingency plan will – or so we hope – have planned for the establishment of a new means of exchange, such as compensatory exchange – a means of trade practised much more widely than generally realised in the nations of the Third World, and now in eastern Europe as well as in the former Soviet Union.

This scenario of the 'end of the western world' is much less surprising, in fact, than the end of the communist régime in the Soviet Union which we witnessed in 1991. One might perhaps compare the weaknesses and the faults of the Communist Party with the weakness and faults of the bankers. Both will have been grave-diggers for systems which fundamentally had some good qualities.

Convinced of the death of communism by the collapse of the Soviet Union, the West has forced the inheritors of that régime to adopt the

---

[24] Jean Gimpel, John Seymour and Lady Elton, 'An emergency plan for our civilisation' in *Social Innovation – a compendium*. Published by The Institute for Social Inventions (London, 1993).

market economy by not revealing to them the terrible economic and financial ills which afflict us. We are like a seriously ill patient who recommends his illness to a dying man.

When our system collapses and we live in economic and political chaos somewhat similar to current conditions in the former Soviet Union, we will be experiencing the disintegration of our industrial civilisation.

The disappearance of information technology from everyday life will be the first factor to undermine society. In chapter 2 I attempted to show that the micro-electronic revolution only happened once, and that from the middle of the 1980s its expansion ceased. With the crumbling of our industrial system, power cuts and frequent fluctuations of voltage will render much computer data unusable. The post-civilisation period will see a tragically expanding crisis of information technology.

This failure will deprive computers of the fundamental data indispensable for the conquest of space, which will henceforward have to await future civilisations, a rendezvous postponed for several centuries. Aeronautical manufacturing, already in crisis, will be another distressed industry. The consequences will affect the West as much as the countries now referred to as 'developing'. In effect, the risk of a very serious drop in production of long-distance carriers will prevent the air companies (which are also in crisis) from renewing their fleets. It may no longer be possible to cross the Atlantic. The countries of the Third World will be increasingly isolated. The globe, so closely knit together in the twentieth century, may once more become a world in which future explorers will have to rediscover distant countries and lost islands in the midst of the oceans.

Difficulties will not be limited to space but will extend to land communications too. Just as after the fall of the Roman Empire, bridges and roads will fall into disrepair, paralysing commerce between regions and nations.

Industries, lacking raw materials and foreign currency, will largely close down except for those which have been able to acquire stocks through balanced exchange. This in fact is how certain industries survive today in the East, through ingenuity.

Because of petrol rationing, traffic will be automatically much reduced – for years I have been telling complaining taxi drivers that traffic jams are the price of prosperity, that the day when there are no more traffic jams will be the day when there is virtually no more petrol and when their former passengers will be too poor to afford a taxi.

The only people to enjoy disindustrialisation will no doubt be certain ecologists who will congratulate themselves at finally seeing the ozone layer preserved. Let us hope that they will be reconverted and will apply the same enthusiasm which they have employed for saving various animal species into saving the human race.

The end of white supremacy

But we should take heed of the fact that deindustrialisation will mainly happen in the west and in the former Soviet Union, and that this dramatic trend will mark the end of 500 years of European domination of the world. In a very pertinent book, Pierre Lellouche[25] wrote in 1992 that, when the USA and the Soviet Union were confronting each other, mankind was witnessing the encounter of two ideologies, the democratic and the marxist, created by our white reigning civilisation. When capitalism and democracy collapses in the west, as I predict it will following the bankruptcy of our financial system after the disintegration of marxism in the Soviet Union, we will very possibly be witnessing the twilight of the white race – provisionally we hope.

As is now generally recognised, the centre of world trade has moved from the Atlantic to the Pacific. In 1982, the volume of trade across the Pacific overtook that across the Atlantic. The developing countries in the Far East grew in 1993 by 7.4 per cent compared with the world's 0.6 per cent. Nevertheless, when Wall Street crashes, triggered off perhaps by a sharp fall of shares in Tokyo, Hong Kong or Singapore, the Pacific Basin will suffer an economic deceleration. But in the long run the Far East will recover progressively, achieving world economic supremacy while the former countries of our once glorious civilisation will become, in their turn, developing countries.

China will progressively dominate the Pacific Basin and beyond and, for the second time in her long history, she will have entered an era of growth in which her psychological drive and her technological evolution will rise in parallel curves. China is at the beginning of a cycle that could last a millenium, while western civilisation stands at the end of a cycle that is already 1,000 years old.

---

[25] Pierre Lellouche, *Le Nouveau Monde – De l'ordre de Yalta au désordre des nations.* (Paris, 1992).

Bibliography

The References in this book are given as footnotes. This bibliography is an alphabetical listing of these references. Authors names are also included in the Index.

ABEL, Armand
La place des science occultes dans la decadence IN Classicisme et Declin culturel dans l'histoire de l'Islam, Maisonneuve et Larose, Paris, 1977

AGARWAL, Anil
Mud, Mud, Earthscan, London, 1981

ANDERSON, Ian
Animals show how microgravity grinds you down New Scientist 25th Feb 1989 p 26

ATHEA, Nicole etc
"Procreatique et desinformation" Le Monde 17th Dec, 1987 (other authors Geneviere Delaisi, Laurance Gavarini, Francios Laborie, Joachim Marcus Steiff, Jacques Testard and Anne-Marie de Vilaine)

ATKINSON, William
Working from Home – Is it for you?, IN Tom Forester, Ed, Computers in Human Context, Blackwell, Oxford, 1989 p 218–9

BACHTLER, Barbara
Society no longer trusts science Scientific European, Oct 1990 p 8

BERNAL, J. D.
Science in History, Watts, London, 1964

BOWEN, William
The Puny Pay-off from Office Computers Fortune, 26 May 1986 p 20–24

BROWN, Phyllida
A Model approach to TB New Scientist, 4th Sept, 1993 p 47–48 Burglars swap crowbars for computers New Scientist, 8th April 1989 p 22

BUNYAN, John
Envelope method of treating burns Proceedings Royal Society Medicine 1940, vol 34, p 65–70 (Also more recent memo to author)

CHARLES, Dan
Space may be "too dangerous for human beings". A Report to the American Association for the Advancement of Science New Scientist, 3rd March 1990 p 24

CHER HELICOPTERE
Science et Vie Junior, May 1991 p 10

CIPOLLA, Carlo
The Economic Decline of Empire, Methuen, London, 1970

COLES, Peter
"Non" to man in space Nature 5th May, 1988

COLLIER, Dr Joe
The Health Conspiracy, Hutchinson London, 1982

COSTS M'LUD?
(subject, Cost of manufacture of small aircraft in the USA) Economist, Aug 20, 1988

COULTON, G. C.
Social Life in Britain from the Conquerer to the Reformation Cambridge University Press, Cambridge, 1918

COUSTEAU, Jacques
On board L'Alcyone I celebrated the marriage of the wind and the water Paris Match 1985

CREMERS, Hayo Canter
Locusts Win War with UN New Scientist 8th Jan 1994 p 7

DAVOUST, Emmanuel
La recherche de la vie extra-terrestre La Recherche 1988 no 211 p 828

DE LACY, Justine
The Sexy Computer in Human Context IN Tom Forester, Ed, Computers in the Human Context, Blackwell, Oxford, 1989, p 233

DELATOUCHE, Raymond
La Chretetiente medievale un modele de development Teque, France
1989

DEPARTMENT OF TRANSPORT
The Performance of Concrete Bridges – A Survey of 200 Highway
Bridges, HMSO, London, 1989

DETHIER, Jean
Architecture de Terre, Editions du Centre Pompidou, Paris, 1986

DISSLY, Megan
Super-Tram. How will they change the geography of Europe.
Newsweek, 31st July 1989 Front page cover
Doubts over long term space flights after cosmonaut's death Nature 18th
Aug 1988 p 557

DROUIN, Pierre
L'Autre Futur, Fayard, Paris 1989

DUCROCQ, Albert
Tomates suspects Sciences et Avenir December 1990 p 15

DUPLAN, Christian etc
Informatiques, les Perceurs de Secrets L'Express 3rd March 1988 p 95
(other authors Vincent Giret and Laurent Meyniard)

DUTTON, Diana
Worse than the Disease – Pitfalls of Medical Progress, Cambridge
University Press, Cambridge, 1988

EDELMAN, Bernard Experimentation sur L'Homme La Recherche, Sept
1991 p 1065

FARRINGTON, Benjamin
Francis Bacon – Philosopher of Industrial Science, Lawrence and
Wishart, 1951

FATHY, Hasson
Architecture for the Poor, University of Chicago Press, Chicago, 1973

FORESTER, Tom, Ed.
Computers in the Human Context – Information Technology,
Productivity and People, Basil Blackwell, Oxford 1989

FRANKE, Richard H.
Technology Revolution in Productivity Decline: The case of US Banks IN
Tom Forestor, Ed, Computers in the Human Context, Blackwell, 1989
p 283 Free Wheeling The Economist 12th Feb 1989 p 32

GAUDIN, Thierry etc
The Intelligent Revolution – a European Report on the State of
Technology, translated and adapted by the Gamma Institute Press,
Canada, 1983

GIARINI, Orio and LOUBERGIE, Henri
The Diminishing Returns of Technology, Pergamon Press, Oxford, 1978

GILLE, Bertrand
The Engineers of the Renaissance, Lund Humphries, 1966

GIMPEL, Jean
The Cathedral Builders, Edition Seuil, 1958, Pimlico, 1993 (English
Edition)

GIMPEL, Jean
The Greying of America National Review 26th Nov 1976 p 1284–1288

GIMPEL, Jean
The Medieval Machine, the Industrial Revolution of the Middle Ages,
Pimlico, London, 1992

GIMPEL, Jean, SEYMOUR, John and Lady ELLTON
An Emergency Plan for our Civilization IN Social Innovation. A
Compendium, Institute of Social Inventions, London, 1993

GIMPEL, Rene
The Diary of an Art Dealer, Pimlico, London, 1991

GLUBB PASHA (Sir John Glubb)
The Fate of Empires Blackwood's Magazine, Dec 1976 p 484–511

HAGUE, Sir Douglas
Selfish Scientists Expect Pennies from Heaven New Scientist 16 Sept 1989
p 27

HARVEY, Brian
Race into Space – the Soviet Space Program, Ellis Horwood, Chichester, 1988

HILL, Donald and AYMED Y-AL-HASSAN
Islamic Technology, Cambridge University Press, Cambridge, 1986

HUBER, Peter W.
Liability Law: The Enemy of Innovation, Policy Forum, The Cato Institute, 1986

HUBER, Peter W.
Liability – The Legal Revolution and its Consequences, Basic Books, New York, 1988

HUBER, Peter W.
"Memo to scientists: Stop innovating" The Scientist, 11th Jan 1988 p 13

HUBER, Peter W.
Who will protect us against our protectors? Forbes, 13 July 1987 p 64

HUSSEL, Marie-Jeanne
Bioethique: faut-il une loi? Sciences et Avenir, 1990

ILO
Small scale manufacture of stabilised soil blocks Technological Memorandum no 12, ILO Technology Series, Geneva 1987

IBN KHALDUN
Les Prolegomenes. Translated by M de Slane, Paris, vol 1 p 263, 1934

JAMMA, Corinna
L'offense des Maladies Tropicales Sciences et Avener, Oct 1989 p 93
Japanese Studies in the History of Science, Nippon Magazaki Caklai, Tokyo, 1962

KAHN, Herman and WIENER, Anthony J.
The Year 2000, MacMillan, New York, 1968

KELLER, A. G.
A Byzantine Admirer of Western Progress: Cardinal Bessarion Cambridge Historical Journal Vol XI, 1995

KENNEDY, Donald
The Overselling of American Science New Scientist, 21st Jan 1989 p 30

KOESTLER, Arthur
The Sleepwalkers Hutchinson, London, 1959, Penguin Paperback First published 1968

KRAMISH, Arnold
The Limits of Science and High Technology, Personal Memorandum to the author, 1988

KRANZBERG, Melvin
The Information Age IN Tom Forester, Ed, Computers in the Human Context, Blackwell, Oxford 1989 p 20

LANDES, David
The Prometheus Unbound – Technical change and Industrial Development in Western Europe from 1750 to the Present, Cambridge University Press, Cambridge, 1969

LASFARGUE, Yves
Technojolies, Technofolies Les Edition d'Organisation, 1988

LELLOUCHE, Pierre
Le Nouveau Monde – De L'ordre de Yalta au desordre des nations, Grasset, Paris, 1992

LEVINE, Israel
Francis Bacon, Leonard Parsons, 1925

LILLEY, S.
Man, Machines and Men, Cobbett Press, 1948

LOVE, Jamie
Scientists' attitudes to weapons. Nature 27th Oct, 1988 Letter p 758

LUST, Reimar
Europes space plans. The Scientist 11th Jan, 1988

MADDOX, John
Is there a future for research? Nature 20th July 1989 p 183

MANSER, Jose
Timber constructed homes Building Homes Supplement 11th Aug 1989 p 30

MEIKLE, Jeffrey
Nylon, the Golden Age of Legs and the Progress of Plastic. The International Herald Tribune 19th Jan, 1988

MERCIER, P. etc
La Societe digitale – Les nouvelles technologies au futur quotidien, Seuil, Paris 1984

MOREAU, David
Malady without a cure The Chemical Engineer, 1988, June 2rd, p 33

MORIN, Edgar
Science avec conscience, Fayard, Paris, 1982 OECD Technical Change and Economic Policy, OECD, Paris, 1980

RICKOVER, Admiral
Evidence of Admiral Rickover to the Joint Economic Committe, US Senate Washington, Stenographic Transcripts AGE-Federal Reporters, 28 Jan, 1982 [Reported in New York Reviews of Books, 18 March 1982, p 19]

RILEY, James C.
Sickness, Recovery and Death. A History of Forecasts of Ill Health, MacMillan, London, 1989

ROSE, Philippe
La Criminalite Informatique, Pue, Paris 1988

ROUSSEAU, Jean Jacques
Confessions. Many editions. First published 1782

RUSSO, Margharita
Technical change and the Industrial District. The role of inter-firm relations in the growth and transformation of ceramic tile production. IN Goodman, Edward, ed. Small firms and Industrial Districts in Italy, Routledge, London, 1989 p 198

SALOMON, Jean-Jacques
Science, Guerre et Paix, Economica, 1989 p 25

SALOMON, Jean-Jacques
Promethee Empetre. Le Resistance au Changement Technique, Editions Anthopos, Paris, 1984, First edition Pergamon Press 1981

SARTON, George
A History of Science, Harvard University Press, Cambridge, Mass. 1959, Oxford University Press, Oxford, 1959

SCHMIDT, William E.
Amtrak strains to get aboard International Herald Tribune, 14th March 1989

SCHWARTZ, Laurent
Velo: L'Innovation pousse a la roue. Sciences et Avenir, July 1991 p 74, 77

SHADMON, Asher
Stone, Intermediate Technology Publishers, London, 1989

SHARPE, Tom
Me and my Word Processor The Listener 25th April 1985

SIDONIUS
Poems and letters, translated by W. R. Anderson. London and Cambridge, Mass. 1836

SIMMONS, Adele and SANBONMATSU, John
Overarmed Earth could go the way of Challenger International Herald Tribune, 10th Feb. 1988

SMITH, Randolph
False Prophesies – From cancer to the common cold predicting a cure has been easier than coming up with one Wall Street Journal 13 Nov, 1989, p 12

SOULAT, Claude
TDF-I/TDF2: Les Monstres de L'Espace L'Obs Economie 3–9 Jan, 1991 p 45

SPACE IS FAR OUT
New Scientist 2 Sept 1989 p 21

SPENGLER, Oswald
The Decline of the West, 2 vols, 1926/28 Allen and Unwin, London

SPENGLER, Oswald
Man and Technics, London, Allen and Unwin, 1932, Reprinted by European Book Society, London, 1992

SWIFT, Jonathan
Gulliver's Travels Many editions. First Published in 1726

SWINBANKS, David and ANDERSON, Christopher
Japan stubs its toes on fifth generation computer Nature 26th March 1992, p 273/4

TAYLOR, John Gerald
Superminds, MacMillan, London, 1975

TESTARD, Jacques
Manifesto, Maitriser la Science Le Monde 19th March 1988

TOFFLER, Alvin
Future Shock, Bodley Head, London, 1971 Pan paperback 1992

TOFFLER, Alvin
The Third Wave, William Collins, London, 1980, Pan paper back 1982

UNIVERSITY OF SOUTHERN CALIFORNIA
Seminar – The Future of the West, University of Southern California, 17–19th March 1977

WARD, Colin
Can they make jobs too? The Italian Lesson, Welcome in Inner City, Bedford Square Press, London, 1989

WHITE, Lynn Jr.
The Expansion of Technology 500 – 1000 IN Fontana Economic History, Fontana 1969, vol 1 p 24

WHITE, Lynn Jr.
Cultural Climates and Technological Advances in the Middle Ages, Viator, 1971

WHITE, Lynn Jr.
Medieval Religion and Technology: Collected Essays, University of California Press, California, 1975

With the Future of Satellites very much in the air, it pays to have your feet on the ground What Satellite TV, March 1994 p 12

Index

HARDBACK
THE END OF THE FUTURE

ISBN 0-7449-0117-0

9 780744 901177